PAT M. ASHWORTH qualified as a n for more than twenty years in clinic care. After graduating with an ` Manchester in 1976 she moved into research and also taught nursing there, and in 1985 she became a Senior Lecturer in the Department of Nursing at the University of Ulster, in Northern Ireland where she continues to live.

Already a member of Nurses Christian Fellowship in England, she first experienced NCFI at a conference in Austria in 1964, and later became more active in various aspects of the Fellowship's work. Involvement in NCFI and other professional nursing activities continued long after 'retirement'.

A HISTORY OF
NURSES CHRISTIAN
FELLOWSHIP
INTERNATIONAL

The First 50 Years

PAT M. ASHWORTH

BLACKSTAFF PRESS

BELFAST

First published in 2012 by
Blackstaff Press
4c Heron Wharf
Sydenham Business Park
Belfast BT3 9LE

and Nurses Christian Fellowship International
Annandale
11A Kirkintilloch Road
Lenzie
Glasgow G66 4RW

Typeset by CJWT Solutions, St Helens
Printed in Great Britain by the MPG Books Group

A CIP catalogue record for this book is available
from the British Library

ISBN 978-0-85640-071-1

www.blackstaffpress.com

www.ncfi.org

Nurses Christian Fellowship International (NCFI) is a charity registered
with the Charity Commission for England & Wales.
Registration No: 258936

CONTENTS

GUIDE TO TERMS

ACE	Asociación Cristiana de Enfermeras Chilenas (Christian Association of Chilean Nurses) – Chile
AFES	Australian Fellowship of Evangelical Students
ANZEA	Australia, New Zealand and East Asia – NCFI Region
CAME	Central Asia and the Middle East – NCFI Region
CNA	Canadian Nurses Association
CANA	Caribbean and North America – NCFI Region
CEF	Campus Evangelical Fellowship
CMF	Christian Medical Fellowship – UK
CMS	Christian Medical Society – USA
CNF	Christian Nurses Fellowship – USA
CNI	*Christian Nurse International* – NCFI publication
CNM	Christian Nurses and Midwives – UK
CNR	Council of National Representatives – NCFI
CPCS	Christian Perspectives Consultative Summit
CPF	Christian Ploughman Fellowship – Taiwan
CSN	Christian Student Nurses – UK
CTN	Christian Therapists Network – UK
CUNSA	Canadian University Nursing Students Association
CYL	Christian Youth League – USA
DHK	Danske Hospitalers Kristne Kreds (Christian Circle of Danish Hospitals) – Denmark
DKS	Dansk Kristelig Sygeplejeforening (Danish Christian Nursing Association) – NCF Denmark
EMF	Evangelical Medical Fellowship – Japan
ENFI	Evangelical Nurses Fellowship of India – NCF India
FCN	Fellowship of Christian Nurses – NCF Nigeria
FCS	Fellowship of Christian Students – Nigeria
FNA	Finnish Nurses' Association – Finland
GBU	Grupo Bíblico Universitario – Chile
HCF	Hospital Christian Fellowship

HCFI	Hospital Christian Fellowship International; also known as International Hospital Christian Fellowship (IHCF); later to become Healthcare Christian Fellowship International / International Healthcare Christian Fellowship
HKEFS	Hong Kong Evangelical Fellowship of Students
HKNCF	Hong Kong Nurses Christian Fellowship
ICN	International Council of Nurses
IDDP	Impact Discipleship Development Programme – Nigeria
IFES	International Fellowship of Evangelical Students – UK
IHCF	*see* HCFI
IHNCF	Inter-Hospital Nurses Christian Fellowship – England, Wales and Northern Ireland
IVCF	Inter-Varsity Christian Fellowship
IVFC	Inter-Varsity Fellowship of Canada
IVP	Inter-Varsity Press
JBS	Japanese Bible Society
JCMA	Japan Christian Medical Association
JCN	*Journal of Christian Nursing* – NCF USA publication
JNCF	Japan Nurses Christian Fellowship
KCNA	Korea Christian Nurses Association
KFH	Kristen Forening for Helsepersonell (Christian Association For Health Personnel) – Norway
KFSS	Kristent Forum for Sykepleiere og Sykepleierstudenter (Christian Forum for Nurses and Nurse Students) – Norway
KNAS	(Contrast to New Age in Nursing) – Denmark
KNCF	Korea Nurses Christian Fellowship
MOCEP	Movimiento Cristiano de Enfermeras Peruanas (Christian Movement of Peruvian Nurses) – NCF Peru
NCFA	Nurses Christian Fellowship Australia
NCFG	Nurses Christian Fellowship Ghana
NCFI	Nurses Christian Fellowship International

NCM	Nurses Christian Movement – Australia
NEC	National Executive Council – Nigeria
NEF	Nurses Evangelical Fellowship – Taiwan
NGC	National General Council – Nigeria
NKSS	Norges Kristelige Student og Skoleungdomslag (Fellowship of Evangelical Students) – Norway
NNCF	National Nurses Christian Fellowships
NNCF	Nepal Nurses Christian Fellowship
NULCI	Nurses for Life Community Initiative – Nigeria
OMF	Overseas Missionary Fellowship
PACEA	Pacific and East Asia – NCFI Region
PNA	Philippine Nurses Association
PNG NCF	Papua New Guinea Nurses Christian Fellowship
SIM	Sudan Interior Mission
SNCF	Singapore Nurses Christian Fellowship
SSKS	Sjuksköterskornas Kristliga Förening (Finnish Nurses Christian Fellowship) – NCF Finland
SUM	Sudan United Mission
UCCF	Universities and Colleges Christian Fellowship
UCEA	Unión Cristiana de Enfermeros en Argentina (Christian Union of Argentinian Nurses) – National Nurses Christian Fellowship Argentina
UME	Unión Médica Evangélica de España (Spanish Christian Medical Fellowship) – Spain
WHO	World Health Organisation
ZNCF	Zambian Nurses Christian Fellowship

ACKNOWLEDGEMENTS

In this relatively short account of the first fifty years of Nurses Christian Fellowship International (NCFI), following its constitution in 1958, it is impossible to do justice to all those who were involved in the history recorded. This is an attempt to make sure that we do not lose the early part of our overall NCFI story as the years pass, because it can be a source of learning and encouragement. I hope that others may write more history, perhaps at regional or national level, giving more personal accounts of the importance of NCFI to nurses and nursing, and the people they serve, in their area of the world.

This account of the early history of NCFI draws heavily on two short histories entitled *Highway: A short history of the Nurses Christian Fellowship International* (1969) and *Continuing the Highway* (1974), both written by Miss Johan Allan. Miss Allan was NCFI's first elected President (a position she held for seventeen years), full-time Secretary to NCFI from 1969–74 and, perhaps most importantly, a key figure in the initial meetings to discuss the formation of an international fellowship.

Other main sources throughout this history are the official minutes of NCFI committee meetings, staff reports and news and prayer letters, and other NCFI publications. I am also grateful to the National NCFS (NNCFS) who provided material on their own organisations.

Thanks are due to those on several continents (including Ruth Lichtenberger, the first General Director) who kindly read and checked the main history content some time ago for errors and omissions. My apologies for any inaccuracies which remain.

Thanks are also due to those who took the photos, or appear in them, since pictures help to bring history to life – it is a joy to be able to see again and remember those who are no longer with us for whatever reason. Many of these images were retrieved from the Maidstone NCFI office before it was closed, and they provide an invaluable insight into our history.

I am also grateful to Mr Alan Leighton, photographer, who transformed many of the images into digital form, and to the staff of Blackstaff Press, who finally brought the book to birth.

INTRODUCTION

N CFI has made a difference to nursing, nurses, and the people in contact with them in many countries around the world. Its history therefore has significance not only for Christian nurses but for others too, and should be recorded. But to understand it some knowledge of the context is necessary.

Nursing and nurses do not exist in a vacuum. As people, nurses are usually very much involved in the life of the community and country in which they live – as individuals, as wives or husbands, as parents or as carers for people of older generations, perhaps as part of a church or other religious or social community. As nurses, they may provide healthcare for people of any race and part of society, with any physical and mental condition, and at any age from conception to death, although obviously midwives and some nurses focus on the care of people within a particular age range, condition or situation. Nurses are affected, perhaps more than most other people, by the many economic and political changes and crises, wars, famines, floods, earthquakes and other natural disasters which occur around the world, as well as the considerable discrepancies in distribution of resources. So it is necessary first to address the world and nursing context which must be taken into account when considering the history of NCFI.

The world has changed very much in fifty years, and one of the major areas of change is technology which, like most of what God has given us, can be used for bad or good purposes. While advances in communication have led to quicker dissemination of information, keeping us abreast of world events and thereby enabling us to respond to many humanitarian crises much more quickly and effectively, frequent news coverage and images of disasters or long-term distress have meant that many people are used to seeing and hearing about them, and some may become less inclined to take action to help. Easier, faster and increased methods of travel may mean that the world really has become a global village, but this too can be to our detriment as far as the potential spread of infections is concerned. Combined with this is the emergence of new diseases and viruses, such as HIV and AIDS which have such a devastating effect on whole populations in some parts of the world.

In nursing too there have been changes. In the 1950s most nurses' work was much more focused on following routines and doctors' orders, and many health systems were still very much hospital-based. This is still the case in some countries, but things are changing. In at least some countries there is a tendency to shift the focus of healthcare into the community (where it has always been from necessity in some areas, though inadequately resourced).

Developments in medications and medical technology mean that many more patients can have a longer active life with less disability and discomfort. But to achieve this requires more nursing input based on broader knowledge and skills. It places demands on nurses, many of whom now take on much more responsibility, work more independently and with personal professional accountability. The increase in responsibilities and independence can bring benefits to nurses and their patients, enabling nurses to provide real care for suffering people, but they can also lead to more pressures from work. Nurses often suffer from work overload; can be faced with ethical dilemmas; and can experience an increased sense of frustration when resources are not adequate to do what is known to be technically possible. In the same way, many nurses struggle to meet the basic economic needs of their families or, in more prosperous countries, the higher expectations of their families in a high consumption society.

In many countries now student, and sometimes qualified, nurses require higher education in universities to equip them better to meet present and future intellectual, psychological and physical demands. These changes to nurse education, while necessary to prepare nurses for all this, also make different demands on students, academic teachers and nurses in practice. Changes in nursing management, originating not only from nursing and nurse education, but also from many other social, cultural, political and economic factors, also make demands and may bring conflicts between honest provision of good care and treatment and what is possible within legitimate resources.

It is not surprising that stress is a well-known concept in nursing.

Nurses, therefore, need sources of continuing strength and refreshment, and of spiritual health and growth, if they are to continue to function fully as effective nurses. Organised nursing in most countries has roots in Christianity, and many of the nurses and nurse leaders involved in developing the profession were or are Christian. Their faith has both sustained them and helped to shape the values of nursing widely acknowledged now.

The International Council of Nurses Code of Ethics, first accepted in 1953 and revised and reaffirmed several times since then, indicates the high standards expected of nurses. It asserts, 'Nursing is unrestricted by considerations of age, colour, creed, culture, disability or illness, gender, nationality, politics, race, or social status.' An honourable doctrine, yet it has presented challenges to nurses in societies and situations where there is discrimination against people on such grounds. It has often been difficult or even dangerous, and still is in some places, for nurses to work according to such values when this contradicts the expectations of their human and political environment.

For such reasons nurses often feel the need for more than human help and support, and their faith becomes even more important – it sustains them, as well as providing the motivation for their work. But attendance at church meetings can be difficult, and often impossible, due to the long, frequently unsocial, working hours that nurses keep. So in the twentieth century (or perhaps even before that) nurses in some countries set up Christian fellowship groups that would meet, mainly in hospitals, to sustain Christian nurses and enable them to share their faith and resources with others. Over time these groups became referred to as Nurses' Christian Fellowships (NCFs) – though often any nurse was welcome to attend. Midwives have always been included amongst the members of Nurses' Christian Fellowships since, while not all midwives are nurses, in some countries many are. Both nurses and midwives provide healthcare for people at challenging times in their lives, although midwifery focuses on care for healthy rather than sick people. When there were a number of groups in a country where communication, organisation and so on were reasonably possible, they joined together to form a national NCF (NNCF).

Since the formation of those early groups, however, much has changed for the NCFs. Most nurses no longer live together in hospital nurses' homes, but are scattered in their own homes, often with family responsibilities. Society has, in some places, become more secular, more multicultural and multifaith, and/or more prone to New Age ideas and practices in some of the countries which have considerable influence on nursing globally. This is reflected in some of the nursing literature, and in some education and practice. Because of lifestyle changes and choices, NCFs have changed in some places from mainly weekly hospital group meetings in hospital premises, to less frequent meetings or conferences, often addressing a professional issue from a Christian perspective, and include other activities to address the needs of nurses. Some NCFs have grown smaller or even ceased (and perhaps been reborn later); others have grown in size, often those more recently established and in different parts of the world from some of the NCFs which developed earlier. It is not surprising that with NCFs in very varied countries and situations, they face some different local problems and needs, and develop different ways of meeting them. But in 1978, in an article on the future of nursing, one Christian nurse outlined the fundamental changes that could be seen in many places. As she observed, nursing was moving:

1) from reactive to scientific
2) from institutionalised to individualised
3) from routinised to creative
4) from dependent to accountable
   (McFarlane, 1978, 5)

The Christian family is worldwide, and so is the family of nursing, and the challenges of being part of both are considerable everywhere. So there is much that nurses share, particularly Christian nurses, and much to be learned from each other, as well as sharing resources and support. It is within the context described so far that Nurses' Christian Fellowship International began and developed.

PART I

A HISTORY OF
NURSES CHRISTIAN FELLOWSHIP
INTERNATIONAL
THE FIRST 50 YEARS

1

THE CONCEPTION AND BIRTH OF NCFI

It was in Keswick, England in July 1956 that nurses from different countries first met to consider the possibility and advisability of an international Fellowship, but before this there had been informal links and correspondence between Christian nurses and fellowships. For example, between 1946–56 Miss Johan Allan, MBE, SRN, SCM, Honorary Secretary to the Scottish NCF and later Matron of a hospital in Malta, had approached nurses from other countries who were visiting Britain, to try to find out if NCFs existed in their countries.

And in 1951 two workers (neither of them nurses) from the South African Nurses' Christian Fellowship, Mr Francis Grim and Mr Johann Engela, had travelled to Britain and other European countries to visit established NCF groups, encourage and help the small ones, and try to form groups where there were none, before returning to South Africa. As Miss Allan described it, 'these visits were blessed by God, and formed the first direct contact between Nurses' Christian Fellowships of different countries' (Allan, 1969a, 1). Mr Grim 'had been used by God to bring into being Nurses' Christian Fellowship of South Africa' (Allan, 1969a, 1) while Mr Engela was a talented artist whose work was sold, providing an income which was used to help NCF work and finance their travels. 'This is a Biblical principle, if not established, then certainly practised by St Paul, who in his spare time was a tentmaker.' (Allan, 1969a, 1)

In 1956 these two men invited members of NCFs from many countries to meet with them at the annual Keswick Convention (a well-established Christian conference) in England's Lake District. Seventy to eighty people from thirteen countries stayed for several days after the convention to discuss the formation of an international fellowship for nurses. Each day began with a prayer and devotional session led by Miss Mercy Wilmshurst, President of the Inter-Hospital Nurses' Christian Fellowship of England, Mr Grim gave the evening messages, and representatives told of NCF work in their countries. Miss Allan remembered the time with pleasure, '… as they talked and prayed together, it became evident that an International fellowship for nurses was not only possible but highly desirable' (Allan, 1969a, 1). A Basis of Faith was agreed on as a sure foundation on which to build the fellowship and, though reviewed intermittently and later referred to as the Basis of Doctrine (or Doctrinal Basis), it has remained in place. This post-convention gathering of nurses proved so successful that it was decided that another conference should be held the following year.

The second conference, at Oosterbeck, Holland in 1957 was 'specially geared for nurses' (Allan, 1969a, 2). Speakers from among those attending aimed to clarify various points of doctrine in the agreed Basis of Faith, and again there was an exchange of news and views amongst participants. One hundred and forty representatives came from twenty widespread countries, from Iceland to New Zealand, and two members from each country were chosen to form the General Committee, which met between sessions 'to define the aims of the Fellowship, and outline a framework within which they could be carried out' (Allan, 1969a, 2). This trial constitution was drawn up in sixteen hours, a surprisingly short time, given language difficulties and different possible shades of meaning of words. The constitution was referred to the national NCFS (NNCFS) for their comments, and a Caretaker Committee was formed with Miss Agnes Thompson of Scotland appointed as Honorary Secretary, to hold office until the conference the following year. When the time came to choose a name, the words Nurses' Christian Fellowship International were tried in every possible configuration, the final order being chosen because the emphasis is placed on nurses, for whom the Fellowship was intended. As a Christian organisation NCFI from the beginning has always been non-denominational and keen to point out that it is not as a replacement for one's own church. As a brochure from the early 1970s states,

> Neither NCFI nor any of its national components is meant to be a substitute for church fellowship, nor its meetings a substitute for church worship. Members are encouraged to help in their local churches and assemblies.

NCFI was becoming established, and it was suggested that well-established NNCFs could aid the development of the Fellowship by 'adopting' a country where Christian work specifically amongst nurses, was only just beginning, offering help by prayer, gifts and possibly visits of workers.

At the third conference, held in Moscia, Switzerland in 1958, there were one hundred and twenty nurses representing twenty-two countries. Speakers included Mr Grim, who gave the morning Bible studies, Drs Hans and Agathe Burki from Switzerland, and Revd William Nagenda of Uganda who spoke in the evenings.

A conference pattern was emerging. Morning prayer meetings – led by different countries in turn – morning Bible study; early afternoon free; late afternoon report sessions; evening talks – all added up to a profitable spiritual experience. No doubt there was also amongst nurses the joy of meeting 'old' as well as new friends who shared Christian and nursing interests, and expanding networks and prayer. It appeared that the 'adoption' scheme was working. Switzerland was helping Germany, Sweden visiting Greece, Scotland adopting France, and England helping Italy. (Allan, 1969a, 2)

This time General Committee Meetings followed the conference and, as the emphasis was now definitely on nurses, Mr Grim asked Miss Johan Allan to take his place in chairing these – a move welcomed by the committee. Each NNCF was now represented by two people it had appointed, while countries without any established NCFs were represented by individuals who had been granted membership in NCFI due to their interest in it, and in the formation of an NCF in their country.

At the meetings, the main focus was on laying the foundation upon which NCFI would build. The Constitution was discussed, altered where necessary, and ratified by the committee, and new memberships were considered. Word of NCFI had spread, and the Caretaker Committee had already received applications for membership from NNCFs (or their equivalent) of Australia, Iceland, Israel, New Zealand, Scotland, South Africa, Sweden and Switzerland. Acceptance for membership was confirmed by the General Committee, who would examine each country's Basis of Faith and ensure that it was compatible with NCFI's and vice versa.

The financial needs of NCFI were also examined at these meetings and it was agreed that, while NNCFs should feel responsibility for these, 'this was largely a work based on faith that God would supply the needs' (Allan, 1969a, 3). So it was agreed that each NNCF was to give to NCFI the amount they felt was their due contribution, after receiving NCFI's budget for the year ahead.

It had become very clear that an executive committee, a secretary and an office were necessary. The members of the General Committee nominated members for and elected the first Executive Committee, which was to meet annually. Miss Allan was asked to become the first President of NCFI and accepted this honour, while Anna-Svea Andersson from Sweden became the much-respected Vice-President, remaining in office until 1967. The Scottish delegates, on behalf of their NCF Executive, offered part of their Glasgow offices to accommodate NCFI, and Miss Margaret Smith, the Secretary to NCF Scotland, offered to give part of her time to NCFI work; both offers were accepted gratefully.

2

1958–1967: CONFIRMATION OF THE IDENTITY AND FOCUS OF NCFI

By the end of 1958 NCFI had become, through the leading and providence of God and the vision, faithfulness and efforts of many people of different nations, an established international organisation to support and increase the work of God amongst nurses. The first members, the Basis of Faith on which NCFI is founded, the Aims, Constitution and committee structure, and some administrative facilities were all in place. There were many challenges ahead, but it was exciting to see what had been achieved so far, and that increased confidence to move forward.

The General Committee in 1958 decided that now that NCFI had 'arrived' a conference every third year would be both convenient and sufficient, and the General Committee would meet after each conference. The Executive Committee would meet annually, managing the ongoing work in accordance with decisions made at the General Committee.

The Fellowship continued to grow. At the first Executive Committee Meeting in 1959, Denmark, England and France were accepted as new member countries, and there were many applications for membership from individual nurses, who were encouraged to form an NCF in their respective countries. Applications also came from other healthcare workers and, at the time, it was decided not to form a special section for them, but to accept them as individual members. However by 1960 there were seventy-two applications for individual membership from nurses, medical personnel and friends and it was decided that only nurses should be accepted for individual membership (rescinding the 1959 decision). Other medical personnel would be accepted as associate members, while other people interested in the work NCFI was doing could join as Friends of NCFI in a special section.

The next conference was planned for 1961, in Nyborg Strand, Denmark, but there was a cloud over the proceedings. The leaders of the Danish NCF had adopted a doctrine incompatible with that accepted by NCFI. The doctrine adopted fortunately forbade them to continue the NCF work, but this meant that the Danish NNCF had ceased. This probably had practical implications for those arranging the international conference, as well as causing sadness that the national NCF work in Denmark had ceased. The few remaining groups and individuals had no contact centre, and matrons and other hospital authorities who might have provided facilities tended, because of previous problems, to be suspicious of anyone trying to revive the work in case the problems recurred. Also Iceland resigned its membership as its small NCF was losing nurses who emigrated, and there was a lack of new members coming forward.

Despite these setbacks, two hundred and fifty representatives from twenty-one countries attended the conference, with India represented for the first time by Miss Katie James, an Indian nurse. Work in India had begun in six states, but was not yet united nationally. The challenges of NCF work in such a huge country and population (the vast majority non-Christian) and with so many languages were hard to comprehend for many Europeans, at a time when few nurses travelled so far, unless as missionaries. For the first time also Australian and New Zealand NNCFs were represented by delegates they had sent directly, instead of nurse members who just happened to be in Europe, demonstrating that these NNCFs recognised the importance of NCFI and its work. Fiji NNCF, which received help and support from New Zealand, was warmly welcomed into membership of NCFI.

The few remaining Danish individuals hoping to revive their NCFs found it difficult, with few members and no contact centres in which to meet but, encouraged by the tremendous interest of conference participants, and promises of prayer support, a few Danish nurses felt challenged to begin work afresh. In the months and years that followed, Miss Alma Petersen, a Danish nurse keen to revive an NCF in her country, spent much of her spare time visiting nurses (twice accompanied by the NCFI President) and kept them in touch via newsletter. She continued this work until another full-time worker was found.

Due to the increase in members and in the work it was doing, NCFI now recognised the need for a full-time secretary and an office. Miss

Margaret Smith, who had been combining NCFI work with Scottish NCF work since 1958, felt God's call to the role and was appointed. She found office accommodation in Glasgow almost immediately.

> Events moved quickly after that, proving that this step had the seal of God's approval. An anonymous gift of £100 provided the basic furniture that was needed. There were gifts of necessary equipment, and another gift of several lovely pictures, proving that although God may not supply our wants, He does supply our needs, and adds a few of His own choice luxuries.
> (Allan, 1969a, 5)

In the years that followed, many NCFI members worked to expand the Fellowship's global presence, visiting other countries to renew or make contact with Christian nurses and NCF groups. From 1961–4 Miss Allan, President of NCFI, had visited groups and members in Scandinavia, the Netherlands and, with a Swiss NCF worker, made an exploratory visit to Austria which proved fruitful. Miss Smith, Secretary to NCFI, had visited Iceland with Mr Grim, then Belgium, France and Italy, while in 1962, Dr Agathe Burki, an NCFI Executive Committee member since its inception, visited many South American countries.

Mr Grim had also been travelling widely, awakening the minds of many people to needs and opportunities for Christian work in hospital situations. Increasingly he, and the new countries he visited, became convinced that the Fellowship should include a wider circle of hospital workers. In 1961 the Fellowship in South Africa, in which he was a worker, had changed its name from Nurses Christian Fellowship to Hospital Christian Fellowship (HCF). They, and he, envisaged that the whole of NCFI would change in accord with this concept, and his fieldwork was directed towards this type of Fellowship. Indeed at the 1963 Executive Committee Meeting, from which he was absent, he and a colleague proposed that NCFI should change in this way. However other members of this Committee pointed out that only the General Committee would have the right to make that decision, and it was known that not all its members would agree.

*

The 1964 conference in Alpbach, high in the mountains of Austria, was particularly memorable. Three hundred people, attending the conference from thirty countries, occupied the area's two hotels, two guest houses and all the private accommodation available. The number of visitors approximately equalled the local population, who became accustomed to hearing the greeting '*Gruss Gott*' (literally 'God's greeting to you') in many different accents. Walking to and from the conference hotel between sessions and during free time enjoying the sunshine, coffee and conversation (with nonverbal communication when language failed), participants were refreshed and awed by the views of meadows and wild flowers of the valleys, the mountains all around against the blue sky, and the many other beauties of God's creation. It was an environment which encouraged reflection on the Bible Studies sessions; the talks on the application of Christian principles in hospital work; the information received from nurses of very different countries (including Jordan and Israel); and the prayers members shared, some of which were very evidently answered during the conference.

For the first time two participants were expected from Yugoslavia, beyond the Iron Curtain. All week the conference members waited and prayed for necessary visas and removal of any barriers to travel.

> On the Sunday morning, during a Communion Service, two people quietly entered the hall. They were recognised and Mr Grim was told. He came to the edge of the platform and said, 'All this week we have been praying that our friends from Yugoslavia would be able to come. They have just arrived.' After a few seconds of dead silence, thunderous applause broke out, but far from seeming out of place in such a setting, it was as much an act of worship as the hymns or prayers.
> (Allan, 1969a, 6)

That evening, as Dr Branco Lovrec talked of the challenges faced by Christians in his country, he said, 'Do not think we need more liberty to preach the Gospel openly. Paul's best books were written in prison. John wrote in exile from Patmos. So we do not need more liberty, but more of the Spirit of the Lord.' (Kettle, 1964, 6), a message many would remember, given the context from which it came.

Inevitably the issues of language and translation were important at each of the conferences, and became more so at this one, which was probably the most multilingual so far. Simultaneous translation had been discussed at least since 1960, but was prohibitively expensive so each language group provided its own translator. Although it had always been intended that the language of the conference host country should be the main language, on each occasion it had been necessary to use English, because the translators preferred to translate from English. So those whose first language was English sat at the back, and others who understood it sat at the front. Those who needed translation sat in groups down the sides and in the centre. From the platform the talks were given in English, then in the language of the host country to those in the centre, and translated for the smaller groups at the same time. This system seemed to work well, but inevitably translation made committee work slower; and there were important issues to be discussed.

It had become increasingly evident that two distinct groups were emerging. One group held the original view that a Nurses Christian Fellowship was right and necessary, the other group felt the same about a Hospital Christian Fellowship (HCF). Eight new countries where Mr Grim had travelled, all with Fellowships now constituted as HCFs, had applied for NCFI membership with the implication that NCFI as an organisation would then change to mirror the HCF model. It was a critical time in the Fellowship's development and a topic for debate at the 1964 conference. It had been recognised that, while HCF might be the best, or even only, pattern in some situations, particularly where there were very few Christians in a country, nurses are a large group who work closely with patients, and have some special issues and needs to be addressed.

Revd G.B. Duncan of Scotland, one of the main speakers at the 1964 conference (and internationally well known and respected), was asked to attend the General Committee Meeting which followed the conference, and give the benefit of his advice and experience. He had been at the conference all week, accompanied by his wife, a nurse, and they had talked with many people and could assess the opinions held. His advice after listening to the General Committee discussions was that,

As NCF had been tried and proved, but HCF was still very new, the movement should continue as NCFI until the next conference, and be discussed again, and that the new countries applying with HCFs i.e. Jordan, Lebanon, Portugal, Spain, Southern Rhodesia, Swaziland and Uganda, should be accepted as associate members. (Allan, 1969a, 6)

This, according to the constitution, gave them the right of discussion, without a vote. The Committee accepted this advice. The NNCFs of Norway, Singapore and Trinidad were accepted as new full members, and Norway agreed to host the next conference in June 1967.

Acknowledging that the issue had not been fully settled, NCFI resolved to have everything in order as far as possible before the next conference. Miss Smith paid another visit to France and Iceland, and for the first time travelled to the Faroe Islands, and the Executive Committee received monthly reports from the Secretary on the work and finance, and addressed the work before it. The Committee tried to resolve the major problem discussed at the last General Committee 'so that the conference in Norway would run smoothly, and that there would be as little trauma as possible when the breach, which now seemed inevitable, eventually came.' (Allan, 1969, 7)

NCFI GOES TO THE INTERNATIONAL COUNCIL OF NURSES

In 1964 the Executive Committee decided that NCFI needed to have an official presence at the 1965 International Council of Nurses (ICN) Quadrennial Congress. The ICN is the organisation uniting professional nurses' associations from countries throughout the world. Apart from the staff and an elected board it comprises representatives (two) from only one association in each country which wishes to join. However, apart from the formal business meetings with representatives, the congresses are open to other nurses.

The 1965 congress was being held in Frankfurt, with up to eight thousand nurses expected to attend. Amongst the participants would be some Christians who were members of their NNCFs, others who had not heard of NCF, and some nurses to whom the Gospel was something new. NCFI had recognised the challenges and opportunities this provided, and prayed for guidance on how to respond. Letters arrived from the NCF of Finland and the Lutheran Nurses' Guild of the USA, expressing the hope that Christian nurses could meet at the ICN Congress, and make an impact. The Executive's original vision was to have an attractive stall at the exhibition, displaying literature in many languages, and visited by hundreds of nurses a day, but all efforts to obtain space in the exhibition hall were courteously, and definitely, refused. Instead a plan was made to organise daily prayer meetings and perhaps a luncheon meeting with a good speaker.

Unfortunately, when the congress began – with nearly six thousand nurses from sixty-six countries in attendance – and despite an announcement from the platform, the plan to get those interested together for lunch did not succeed as intended due to failure of the restaurant manager to reserve it as arranged. However with help from the Congress Secretary a very suitable and convenient room was secured for a daily meeting at 1.30–1.55 p.m. The change in arrangements was relayed in person to many who had tried to meet in the restaurant, and notices were displayed – it soon became a pleasant meeting point for many:

> Beginning with twenty-five and rapidly increasing to fifty each day, many nurses met, prayed, shared news, and listened to short devotional and Gospel messages. From Korea one day, the Salvation Army International NCF the next, and so on. Most, because of other commitments, could only attend once or twice, so many came to 'Room 23' during the days of the Congress. A lot, too, was done by personal contact … From Finland to the Philippines, from Frankfurt to Hong Kong, from the specially invited group of students to Executive members of the professional associations of several countries, we felt … that we were 'All one in Jesus Christ.' This must not be an isolated incident. It must be the beginning of a pattern that will continue to be a feature of our national and international professional congresses. These are gatherings of nurses whose lives are spent in the service of

mankind, and who are seeking, in Conference, more effective ways of serving. The emphasis today, as never before, is on treating the 'whole' person, body, soul and mind. We as Christian nurses have the skills in our hands and God's word in our hearts. We should be at the hub of our professional organisations and conferences to show, as St Paul exhorted, 'a more excellent way.' It is a unique opportunity, open to none but ourselves. Let us accept it as a God-given responsibility, remembering that in every situation we are ambassadors for Christ.

(Allan, 1965, 4)

This illustrates the strong vision amongst early nurse leaders in NCFI of the need for integration of Christian nurses' faith with their professional nursing lives. They, like many others later, saw no conflict between vocation and profession.

The success of the NCFI presence at the ICN Congress was a great encouragement to the Executive Committee and, in the years between 1964–66, the Executive Committee minutes recorded more good news. In 1965 the Indian NNCF (ENFI), was formed, and there was news of growth in the Nigerian Fellowship of Christian Nurses (FCN), originally formed in the north of the country in 1960. Australian NCFI member Blanche Lindsay reported spending five weeks in Papua New Guinea, where a small committee was forming an NNCF, while Betty Kettle, Executive Committee member, had found during a study tour that Bodhild Bollerud, a Norwegian Christian nurse who had been at NCFI events, was working with the Danish Fellowship, which now had four NCF groups. There were one hundred and fifty keen members in Switzerland, and in 1966 the NNCFs of Malaysia and Pakistan were accepted into membership of NCFI.

In 1965 Miss Allan spoke of the Professional Developments Committee newly formed within the England, Wales and Northern Ireland IHNCF (the Inter-Hospital Nurses Christian Fellowship, the name for this NNCF at that time, with Scotland having its own, separate NNCF). In the minutes she reported a 'great concern for young nurses growing up in the atmosphere of modern thought, a new morality and other pressures.' The aim of that committee was to influence the nursing profession through its senior members, and lectures were arranged on topics such as teaching ethics, standards, and keeping faith with patients. The work with young people (from 15–18 years of age) wanting to enter nursing had grown and there were three Summer Schools in 1965. The mixture of introduction to nursing, hospital visits, and holiday activities in a Christian context was popular and effective, as some other countries found too.

TWO MAJOR ISSUES OF CONCERN – FINANCE AND FOCUS OF THE WORK

However there were other basic issues of concern. Financial resources of NCFI had never been great, as nurses in most countries had (and in many still do have) relatively low salaries, so the work was built on faith – in God who supplies all resources, and in the faithfulness of people through whom He does so. In 1957 the Committee had decided on a policy of tithing NCFI's income and giving the tithe to some good Christian purpose, but this raised difficulties when there were bills or a salary to be paid and insufficient money to do so. Quarterly financial statements were sent to all NCFI members, and the annual audited accounts to associate members.

In 1965 the Executive Committee expressed concern that the Secretary's salary was so often in arrears and in January 1967 the NCFI President, who had taken over the accounts to relieve the overloaded Secretary, reported that NCFI's spending was higher than its income. Over the previous year the average monthly income had been £134. 5s. 1d; average expenditure £151 12s. 1d; and average monthly deficit £16 (Allan, 1967a, 4). Forty years later, it is difficult to comprehend exactly what those amounts represent, particularly for those unused to British currency. But even at the time, they were small amounts for such an international movement. Expenses were kept to a minimum – office rent (for a Scripture Union room), one paid staff member, stationery and postage, and the production costs for *Highway*, the twelve-page, A5 size, quarterly magazine and the main means of communication within NCFI.

Only three countries were contributing regularly. The £2,000 spent on travel during the year had come largely from the people who had done the travelling, or their immediate and personal friends. Yet such travel was essential for the expansion which had taken place, and would continue to be so. Six ways of helping to improve the financial situation were suggested:

1) Prayer
2) Giving, and using, tax breaks where possible
3) Trading, making things and selling them
4) Promoting *Highway* and collecting subscriptions
5) Saving used postage stamps, which can be sold to dealers
6) Feeling more keenly our responsibility and facing up to it

The Executive Committee Minutes of 1965 recorded that the sale of NCFI diaries was encouraging; but of 1,400 copies of *Highway*, only 420 were sent to subscribers, with 175 sent to missionaries and NCFI individual members, and 700 went to the NNCFs of member countries in batches, for distribution to some of their NCF members (some of whom might be able to pay for them, even if not the full price) or for other purposes. Not all the 1400 copies printed each time were distributed immediately, any remaining being distributed (occasionally sold) at nursing and/or Christian conferences, churches or in other suitable places to provide information on NCFI.

Finance is an issue which has needed attention throughout NCFI's existence, and these responses have continued to be among the most important. Johan Allan ended her article with the words:

Now is the time to find out what God wants of us.
Now is the time to get our priorities right.
Now is the time to take stock of our privileges.
Now is the time to face up to our responsibilities.
Now is the only time we have.
(Allan, 1967a, 4)

These words were equally applicable to the main issue facing the Fellowship, which had become very evident at the 1964 conference – the issue of the name and identity of the Fellowship. Ireland had been accepted for associate membership in 1965 and France had changed to become an HCF, and so its membership was changed to that of associate member. Mr Grim continued to travel, and had visited a number of countries in Latin America, Trinidad and Jamaica, and had made a number of contacts, the visit to Trinidad being especially blessed. However, he continued to promote only the HCF concept in the countries he visited, and at the 1965 Executive Committee meeting, from which he was absent because he was touring South America, the Committee decided that they were unable to co-operate with this, not least because they knew the views of some NNCFs were not in accord with it. But would the HCFs be satisfied to remain associate members? It was felt that neither NCFs nor HCFs were getting the maximum help.

There appeared to be two main alternatives – to change NCFI policy, or for the two groups to separate and pursue their own aims. After discussion it was unanimously decided that it was time to recognise that two movements already existed, and 'could now be organised according to separate aims for the extension of God's Kingdom' (Executive Committee minutes, 1965). The committee members hoped that fellowship between the two movements could be maintained and strengthened and it was agreed that the President and Vice-President would meet with Mr Grim when he reached Europe to discuss this with him, including an expression of apology to him that the different views had not always been well handled.

The Executive Committee drew up policy proposals for submission to the NNCFs and, just before the next conference, a referendum was held among all the member countries. 'They had all been given the facts and a few proposals to discuss with their members.' (Allan, 1969a, 7)

THE 1967 NCFI CONFERENCE – WITH CHANGE IMMINENT

In the meantime, organisation of the 1967 Conference was in hand, with plans for leadership training before it and an international hymn book being prepared by Miss E.J. Wyatt, a missionary nurse. The proposed topics for training were: How to teach Bible study; Problems and questions of faith; A short course in psychology (modern man's problems); Different countries and problems of international work; and Problems of organisation.

There was obviously concern in the Executive Committee that NCFI should be truly international, and there was discussion as to whether Glasgow was the best place for its headquarters. This was a matter for prayer. It was suggested that there should be one non-English article in each issue of *Highway*. In the January–March 1966 issue there was an article in Spanish, but this practice did not continue, presumably because of the cost and logistics of such an undertaking, and the fact that English was the only common language for many people.

Solberg Ungdomsskule, a secondary school in Stavanger, Norway, provided another ideal setting for the conference in 1967. Norway is a beautiful country with mountains, fjords, lakes and rich pastures. The weather was good, and there was much to enjoy – though the sea was too cold for bathing that far north! The venue's main hall had ample, comfortable seating, good acoustics, an organ and piano, and was decorated with the country flags as usual. There were smaller rooms for discussion and country displays, good dining facilities, and the wide main corridor held an attractive bookstall. The three-day leadership course, attended by two to three people from each country, was a new venture, and provided valuable experience for the discussion groups and workshops held during the conference, which were another progressive step.

The conference went well. The three hundred participants from thirty-two countries, mostly nurses with a few doctors and other hospital workers, appreciated the challenging addresses by the Revd George Johnson, Norway, and Miss Muriel Crouch, a surgeon from England, and enjoyed the workshops, report sessions and outings. For the first time each national delegate presented statistical and geographical information, and mentioned political and cultural influences affecting national life, so that their Fellowship report could be seen in context. This was a valuable aid to participants' learning in an age when travel and communication were much more limited, so that they could understand, pray for and perhaps assist each other more intelligently.

But most participants were aware that there were to be big decisions at the General Committee Meetings after the conference, and for some the prospect inevitably overshadowed the pleasant proceedings.

After the conference delegates from eleven member countries (three were not represented), six associate member countries (three others were not represented), nine non-member countries, and the President (Johan Allan), Vice-President (Anna-Svea Andersson), the Field Organiser (Francis Grim), the Secretary/Treasurer, and two other Executive Committee members (four sent apologies) started the serious business facing the General Committee.

After welcoming those present, Miss Allan read Exodus 17:8–13 and Hebrews 4:14–16, and then suggested a short time of prayer. She stressed 'the need for clarity of thought, simplicity of expression, and decisiveness of aim in the discussions to follow'. After other formalities, the meeting began with good news in the Treasurer's Report. Over the previous year there had been expansion in the work and growing interest in many countries. Member countries had provided most of the money to meet NCFI's expenses, but some associate member countries and individuals had also sent gifts. There had also been income from Deed of Covenant gifts (as tax refunds), sale of diaries, used stamps, calendars and other such projects, and all accounts had been paid by the end of the financial year. However only £115 of the £3000 spent on travel for NCFI had come from the funds, and the balance sheet showed current liabilities of £98.11.5d.

The meeting then turned to the main issue – the future of NCFI policy.

NCFI AND HOSPITAL CHRISTIAN FELLOWSHIP INTERNATIONAL (HCFI) – TWO SEPARATE ORGANISATIONS

In 1966 the Executive Committee had drawn up a letter to be sent to all member countries. In it two alternative policy proposals had been outlined for discussion at the General Committee.

1) That the NCFI Constitution be altered (Clause 11) so that the movement could include both Nurses' Christian Fellowships and Hospital Christian Fellowships as members.

2) That in addition to NCFI, an HCFI should be formed, with exchange between the two movements of news, travelling plans, information about new full-time workers, literature, publications etc. Working arrangements would need to be specified.

The National Committees had responded without question as to the validity of postal voting, and so did some of the associate member countries to whom the proposals had been sent just for information. Each country and each Executive Committee member had one vote and, after some debate, it was decided that France and South Africa, the two member countries which had become HCFs after joining NCFI, and Sweden, which was called HCF but was run by nurses, should retain the right to vote until the policy decision was made. All the replies had been sent to delegates before the General Committee, and the votes supported:

Proposal 1	Proposal 2
7 member countries	7 member countries
3 Executive members	5 Executive members
Total: 10 votes	**Total:** 12 votes

Not all were happy with the result, and there were various objections. To the objection that the Executive Committee votes were decisive, the Chairman pointed out that without them the result would be the same, since her casting vote as Chairman would be for Proposal 2. There was much earnest and sometimes emotional discussion including both member and associate member country delegates. Some was discussion among the full committee, and some among two groups supporting the two different proposals. But there was recognition by many that there were already two movements, each seeking to serve God but pursuing different paths.

An Australian delegate, speaking for Group 2 (those supporting

Proposal 2), said that the work of national movements in favour of Proposal 2 was essentially work with nurses and for a number of reasons they wished to continue this. The HCF pattern of work not only included broader membership, which did not always cause difficulty; but it also had as one of its main aims the evangelisation of patients through nurses and medical staff. This was not compatible with the work of many NNCFs, who could not accept the addition of such an aim to the Constitution.

Mr Grim, speaking for Group 1 (those supporting Proposal 1), reinforced the view that the HCF pattern was the way forward, concluding that 'The present Constitution had fulfilled its purpose. Something new and bigger was called for with a wider outreach and wider vision.' (General Committee Minutes, 1967).

There was some very frank discussion among Group 2, which revealed to some countries another problem. Mr Grim, a strong personality, had for some time been acting individually rather than in accord with the wishes of the Executive Committee and some NNCFs. Although working in the name of NCFI, he had not always approached countries through their national committees, and had propagated the HCF concept everywhere he visited, even against the express wishes of the NNCF Committee, as instanced by some delegates. In the last few years no new NCFs had been formed as a result of his visits, and some had been strongly influenced to change to HCF. Efforts had been made to resolve these problems with him directly, but were unsuccessful.

On the advice of the current NCFs group, meetings were arranged to inform representatives of the HCFs group of this additional reason for voting for Proposal 2, with no formal executive structural link between the two organisations which would emerge. This would not prevent the co-operation between the two separate organisations when appropriate, for which hopes had been expressed earlier.

A meeting was also arranged to discuss personally with Mr Grim his intentions regarding future visits to countries with established NCFs. He confirmed that Hospital Christian Fellowship International (HCFI) was in the process of being formed. From this point Groups 1 and 2 met separately. Later the leaders of both groups met to compose the following joint statement which was intended for publication in the literature of each Fellowship concerned, and sent to each country's general Christian press.

The Sixth International Conference of the Nurses' Christian Fellowship International was held in Stavanger, Norway in June 1967. This conference was followed by the General Committee Meetings which were attended by full members, associate members and a group of observers from non-member countries.

For a number of years Hospital Christian Fellowships have been emerging in some countries. At the last International Conference in Austria in 1964 eight of these groups were granted Associate Membership in NCFI without a vote on a trial basis.

A major subject of discussion at the recent committee meetings was that the NCFI constitution be altered to include both Nurses' Christian Fellowships and Hospital Christian Fellowships as full members, or alternatively that in addition to NCFI, an HCFI be formed. It was decided that the wider organisational pattern of the HCF could not be incorporated into NCFI and it was proposed that a parallel international movement be formed to accommodate the Hospital Christian Fellowships.

MEMBERSHIP

In the Nurses' Christian Fellowship International, membership is open to: any National Nurses' Christian Fellowship without discrimination, on agreement with the Doctrinal basis and Aims of the Fellowship. Associate and individual membership is also offered in special circumstances.

In the International Hospital Christian Fellowship: A sound Statement of Faith is the one basic requirement for membership which is open to all National Fellowships in any branch of the Hospital and Health Services. Where no National Fellowships exist, membership is open to Individuals in Hospital and Health Services.
(Allan, 1967b, 8–9)

The statement ended with the addresses of the two headquarters, and was signed by Johan Allan, President of NCFI, and Francis Grim,

International Co-ordinator, IHCF.

In human organisations, even Christian ones, resolution of conflict is often not easy, particularly when the conflict of ideas has been increasingly evident for some years and those involved are from many different nations, cultures and background circumstances. Reading the NCFI minutes of meetings and other references to them, some of the tensions and emotions are evident. The fact that people cared so much about whether a division would occur was perhaps in some ways a sign of what NCFI had achieved so far, as well as vision for its future.

Throughout the discussions and decision-making, people were genuinely trying to follow what they believed was God's plan for the way forward, with proper regard for those with a different perspective. In her introduction to the above Statement in *Highway* Johan Allan wrote,

> I believe that this decision will result in the better working out of the Aims of two distinct trends of thought that have existed until now in NCFI. I believe that God will bless both as they follow the vision He has given them.
> (Allan, 1967b, 8)

Around fifty years later it appears she was right, though relationships between NNCFs and HCFs have not always been easy.

3

1967–76: CONTINUED GROWTH AND DEVELOPMENT

After the decision to form a second movement, only ten countries remained as members of NCFI: Australia, England, Fiji, Israel, Malaysia, New Zealand, Pakistan, Scotland, Singapore and Switzerland. (Norway and Ireland resigned.) No delegates from Fiji, Pakistan, Malaysia and Singapore had been present at the conference that year, but once the representatives from all HCF countries had left the remainder continued with the General Committee Meeting.

It was decided that the headquarters and full-time secretary were still necessary despite the currently reduced membership, as there was more than enough work to do. Amendments to the Constitution were drafted, some of which resulted from the recent organisational changes. A significant change was the addition of a new Aim. The reports, workshops and other contacts at the conference had emphasised that, although God worked in many different ways in different (and sometimes very difficult) circumstances, nurses shared common interests, concerns and challenges. During the 1967 conference, and at the committee discussions afterwards, professional issues and the benefits to the profession of a united witness had been stressed as never before. So the new additional Aim was agreed – 'To encourage the application of Christian principles in professional life.'

The Executive Committee was now to comprise ten members (four of whom need not necessarily be nurses) including the Honorary Officers – at this point the President and Vice-President, since the Treasurer's work was being done by the Secretary or at times the President. The Secretary would be an *ex officio* member. It was not considered appropriate at this time to exclude the possibility of a few non-nurse members of the Executive Committee, since in some countries nurses' lack of hierarchical power, money, higher education, experience of organisation and committee work, and other resources made the help of others not only an advantage but also perhaps a necessity. The fact that nurses were mostly women was also a disadvantage to them in these respects in many countries. However non-nurse Executive Committee members would be a minority, and all the committee members at each meeting signed agreement to the statement of the NCFI Doctrinal Basis and Aims of NCFI (the term Doctrinal Basis here is synonymous with Basis of Faith or Basis of Doctrine, used in different places and times within NCFI and elsewhere). The following were elected to the new Executive Committee: Miss Johan Allan (England) as President, Miss Blanche Lindsay (Australia) as Vice-President, Miss Margaret Smith (Scotland) as Secretary/Treasurer, Dr Agathe Burki and Miss Dora Mettler (Switzerland), and Miss Betty Kettle (England). It was hoped to co-opt others originating from a wider geographical spread.

Plans for the extension of NCFI were discussed and it was agreed that NCFI should, for the foreseeable future, have a stall at the annual Keswick Convention. Also discussed were plans for Executive Committee members to continue making international visits in 1967/8 (where time and finances permitted), and there was a review of the Partnership Plan (originally called adoption). There was no objection to England and Scotland continuing to partner Italy and France (HCF countries), but other young NCFs also needed help. Poland, Hungary, Ghana, Pakistan, Japan and Belgium were mentioned. Ghana had written to ask for practical help, and the Committee thought a partner should be sought. It was proposed that Miss Allan should visit Ghana, and possibly Nigeria, as soon as this could be arranged. Miss Smith might visit Iceland again and possibly Greenland with an Icelandic nurse. Miss Mettler hoped to visit Poland in July, and Dr Burki would visit Hungary in August.

Other suggestions for extension were more courses for leaders, regional training courses for example in Asia, Europe etc., and loan (with salary) of a full-time staff worker or suitable member for two to three months each year to help another country, in collaboration with NCFI. Planned publications included more NCFI pamphlets; a duplicated prayer insert each quarter in *Highway*; diaries for 1968; and possibly the reproduction of Miss Crouch's talks on 'The Spirit of Service', which had been much appreciated during the conference.

The budget for 1967/8 was agreed and would be sent to National Fellowships, who might be asked how much they could contribute.

Plans for NCFI activities at the ICN Congress in Canada in 1969 were already in progress, and possible locations for the next NCFI Conference in 1970 were considered. Finally, there were three suggestions as to possible links with IHCF:

1) Associate membership of NCFI would remain open to HCFs
2) Notification of conferences
3) Exchange of magazines, prayer letters and news to be encouraged between the two International Headquarters, and countries.

A vote of thanks to the President for her conduct of the meetings, which had proved happy in many ways, included reference to her 'sanctified commonsense'. The meeting then closed with prayer.

The prayers of many people had been answered and NCFI was moving forward with its name and focus confirmed, and its Aims expanded. IHCF would also move on, pursuing its vision.

NCFI EXPANSION AND A PILOT NCFI REGION

Johan Allan's offer to visit was accepted by Ghana.

> Five weeks were spent in Ghana, covering 2000 miles of country, talking with leading people in the nursing profession and Christian leaders, visiting hospitals and Community Health Nurses and attempting to assess the position of the Nurses Christian Fellowship work in that country. Four more weeks were spent visiting the Ivory Coast, Liberia, Sierra Leone, Gambia and Senegal.
> (Allan, 1969a, 10)

In Gambia and Liberia key nurses 'caught the vision' of what might be achieved and started working to unite Christian nurses in their witness within their countries. In Ghana a national NCF was established, and it was accepted into membership of NCFI in 1968. In Asia, Blanche Lindsay visited and encouraged the groups in Singapore, Malaysia, Pakistan, Hong Kong and the Philippines in 1967. She reported at the 1968 Executive Committee that Pakistan had twenty-nine groups, but that co-ordination and information were not good. In Eastern Europe persecution seemed to be increasing, especially in Hungary, but it was also encouraging that three Polish nurses felt 'a burden for the work' (Executive Committee Minutes, 1968).

NCFI was active in many parts of the world, and the idea of regionalisation was discussed at the 1968 Executive Committee. It was soon realised that no finance would be saved if regional committees met instead of the Executive, but it was agreed that the idea had merit and so NCFI Vice-President Blanche Lindsay, who would be visiting six other countries on her way home to Australia, was asked to pilot the idea of an NCFI region in ANZEA (Australia, New Zealand and East Asia). The NNCF in Australia had celebrated its Golden Jubilee, while New Zealand's NNCF could claim more than forty years of work. They had assisted Papua New Guinea and Fiji respectively, and missionaries from various countries were supporting development of growing NCF groups in a number of Asian countries. Given the considerable distances involved and difficulties in travel in some places, working as a region would not be easy. But with previous contacts the foundations had been laid, and Blanche Lindsay was known in many places.

It was decided that in a Regional Committee, members should abide by the NCFI Constitution, including the Basis of Doctrine and Aims; that an Executive Committee member should act as chairperson; and that the minutes of the meetings and reports of activities should be sent to the Executive Committee.

During the 1968 Executive Committee meeting members also discussed and outlined the criteria that each NNCF would have to meet before applying for membership of NCFI, and it was agreed that an NNCF should have:

1) a certain number of groups
2) a Doctrinal Basis
3) a representative committee for direction and development of the NCF
4) functioned for at least a year

NCF England had offered reciprocal membership for nurses from other NCFI member countries, and for individual NCFI members if recommended by NCFI. This included the right to serve on committees. The Executive approved of this and hoped other countries would do the same. This would potentially offer considerable advantages to the many nurses who move from one country to another, either temporarily or more permanently, helping them to find Christian contacts and 'settle in' more easily in a new country and culture.

Two other matters which would have important consequences in 1969 were discussed at the 1968 Executive Committee meetings. First, after the successful involvement of NCFI at the 1965 ICN Congress, it had been decided that such opportunities should continue to be used. So plans for the 1969 Congress in Montreal were progressed, in collaboration with the USA and Canadian nurses, for a 'Friendship Lounge' and for several meetings. It was agreed to have a report of the work of NCFI ready for the Congress, so Johan Allan wrote the first short history of NCFI, entitled *Highway*, which was published in 1969. The plans were successfully implemented. Almost 10,000 nurses from 88 countries attended the 1969 ICN Congress, and many of them filled the College Chapel for the Sunday service which began the official Congress activities on 22 June 1969. The NCFI activities began on Monday with the daily continental breakfast at 7.45, followed at 8.00 by a twenty minute message and prayer. The speakers, from the USA, Australia, Canada and England, followed themes including the fact that God was concerned with what went on at the Congress, and the relevance of the Christian message. The 'Friendship Lounge' was much appreciated, as Johan Allan's report shows:

> One and a half tons of New Testaments, gallons of coffee and orange juice, small mountains of rolls, and hostesses on duty from 7.30 a.m. to 6.30 p.m. That was the Nurses' Christian Fellowship lounge ... The chance to rest and be quiet, a place where one's lunch box could be brought and completed by a cup of coffee, a mending basket to cope with the unexpected run in a stocking or dropping hem, a bookstall and plenty of free literature, including newspapers from home, made this a much sought after area ... One of the outstanding features was the spirit of unanimity

amongst the workers. From the various countries, Canada, the USA, New Zealand and England, few had met except within their own country.

(Allan, 1969b, 2–3)

These nurses were already experiencing the spirit of unity and ability to work together which would prove characteristic of NCFI at ICN Congresses, and other activities, even when a much wider variety of nations are involved. Two other successful activities during the Congress were a coffee party and lecture by Dr John White at the Montreal General Hospital, attended by four-hundred people, and the linking of overseas nurses with local Christian families, who entertained them for an evening meal.

A second issue discussed in 1968 was the NCFI Secretary's work. Margaret Smith had been working faithfully in Glasgow handling correspondence and keeping track of every penny coming in and going out, as evidenced by some of the letters found in NCFI papers much later, and it was she who had set up the first NCFI office. But at times she felt rather isolated and, since she had not travelled much recently for NCFI, felt that she lacked up-to-date first-hand news and pictures to convey the needs to others. She had originally been led to believe by Mr Grim that more travel would be involved in the work. However while Margaret was an exceptional Secretary and Treasurer, she was not a nurse, and the Executive Committee felt that if a General Secretary with a wider remit were to be appointed for NCFI, it should be a nurse with post-basic education and administrative experience. This was in accord with the continuing vision of the Executive for NCFI to encourage and help nurses to live out their faith in their profession, and therefore involvement of NCFI in professional affairs.

In 1969 when Margaret Smith was, for the second time, offered a university post she felt God meant her to accept it for further experience and so resigned as NCFI secretary, a post she had held part-time from 1958 and full-time from 1961. In tribute to her Blanche Lindsay, NCFI Vice-President, wrote,

It is not easy to work with an Executive whose members are

scattered in many parts of the world, but Margaret did a very fine job, always keeping us informed with full and regular reports and by setting out all matters requiring decision and action so clearly. We can only guess how often she would have liked to talk and pray with her Executive. A lesser person would have found the responsibility and isolation too great ... We know that we have lost Margaret as a full-time worker, but that we will always have her interest and help. ... Many thanks, Margaret, for your conscientious and faithful service in this difficult time of NCFI development.

(Lindsay, 1969, 8)

Margaret did remain committed to NCFI, providing both short-term help with *Highway* and the 1970 conference, and her financial legacy many years later, which provided important support at a critical time for the Fellowship.

THE FIRST NURSE NCFI SECRETARY

The 1968 Executive Committee had prayed about the need for a trained nurse to be General Secretary and for a more central office, both of which seemed desirable for the future of NCFI. Both of these became reality in 1969. Johan Allan, already President of NCFI, gave up her employment with the General Nursing Council for England and Wales, and became NCFI Secretary, at first temporarily and then permanently, as confirmed by the Executive and 1970 General Committee. Office space became available at the new Church Missionary Society Headquarters in London and, in faith that the relocation was right and money to pay the increased rent would be found, NCFI Headquarters moved to CMS House, 154 Waterloo Road, London. Although this meant losing the fellowship of the close proximity with the Scottish NCF, there were other advantages, such as convenient access for the many nurses who passed through, or were based for a time in and around London; and also more convenient access than previously to other Christian organisations.

Throughout these changes in 1969, the work continued. *Highway* continued to be the main means of general communication, and was sent to eighty-seven countries, though the subscription circulation had not increased. Betty Kettle, an English nurse who had been actively involved in NCFI and the Executive, agreed to edit it and did so for the next few years. Finance for NCFI work remained a concern, though there was a small surplus, rather than a deficit, because of a legacy. But the work was growing. Plans were in progress for the first ANZEA Regional Conference to be held in 1970 with representatives from more than twelve countries expected. In several isolated places in Japan Christian work amongst nurses was in progress, so the Overseas Missionary Fellowship (OMF) were asked if one of their workers could co-ordinate them – helping them to communicate, perhaps encouraging some to meet, co-operating in their activities, seeing if they could share resources in any way. In 1968 (and since Ghana had become a member) Florence Yeboah, a leader in NCF Ghana, had been co-opted to the Executive Committee, so that African views were heard in committee. Though not a nurse, she was a dedicated member of NCFI, and in December 1969 toured Gambia, Sierra Leone, Liberia and Ivory Coast to follow up contacts and make new ones.

THE FIRST SECONDED NCFI STAFF WORKER

In Argentina, Lois Cumming – an English missionary nurse who had been in the country since 1961 – was concerned about the needs of nurses there. Remembering the benefits she had experienced from Nurses Christian Fellowship activities as a young student and nurse, she wanted to start a work amongst nurses in Argentina. Her letter to the English NCF expressing this desire was discussed by Johan Allan with the mission with which Lois worked. The General Secretary there agreed to propose to the local diocese when he visited that Lois be seconded to this work. As a result NCFI took a new step forward in January 1970 when Lois Cumming became the first seconded NCFI staff worker, with the South American Missionary Society responsible for her as a person and NCFI responsible for the work.

Lois was well-prepared for the work. She was a qualified nurse and midwife with a degree in another subject, she spoke Spanish fluently, and was already known to many nurses through her attendance at three National Nursing Congresses in Argentina. As a nurse with a degree (unusual at that time in Britain) she was acceptable to the universities, and had already had opportunity to speak on her work at the three University Schools of Nursing in Argentina. Taking on responsibility for her support was another step in faith by NCFI, as it meant NCFI investing £50 per month in her accommodation and travel. But it was a step which proved fruitful in the foundation of long-term work in Argentina.

THE 1970 NCFI CONFERENCE – NEW INTELLECTUAL CHALLENGES

The seventh NCFI Conference took place on the east coast of Scotland, at that country's oldest university, St Andrews, from 4–14 September 1970, and was preceded by a four-day course for leaders. By this time Ghana (in 1968), Spain (in 1969) and the USA (in 1970) had joined the ten member countries remaining after the previous conference. Around 200 people from 32 countries around the world met for the conference. Formal sessions were in the university lecture hall, and most participants lived in the university residences.

The scene was set on the first day by speaker Dame Muriel Powell, Chief Nursing Officer at the Scottish Home and Health Department, who emphasised the worldwide activity of God in nursing circles, and the need for nurses to be more knowledgeable, technically skilled, while still standing for the truth in love. This was reinforced as the conference proceeded, not least in the intellectual and personal challenges which faced at least some, probably many, participants as revealed by comments below.

On most days there were two main sessions, a late afternoon workshop in groups of ten to twelve people, and an informal after-dinner session. Some national groups prayed together before breakfast and there were many informal groupings for serious, and less serious purposes ... So far it probably sounds a very ordinary conference, but it was anything but that! The difference lay partly

in the fact that the three main speakers, accustomed to lecturing on academic subjects, presented their talks in language and thought-forms unusual to such meetings, and often provocative. How much we needed to listen, think and pray personally during those days!
(Eggo, 1970, 6–7)

The three main speakers were Professor Norman Anderson (theologian), Professor Malcolm Jeeves (psychologist), and Mr Arnold Aldis (a surgeon from Wales), and they obviously presented a challenge to the participants, particularly at a time when nurse education and practice environments (and sometimes churches too) often encouraged, or even required, nurses just to learn and do as instructed, rather than to think and make decisions. Although probably most assented to a similar basis of faith the speakers gave much cause for debate:

> The talks we heard went beyond our points of agreement and faced us squarely with the issues of everyday life in the 1970s for which there is no neat set of commandments in Scripture, and for which we each have our own answers. The possibilities for disagreement were legion! As we lived through the days of the conference together we were aware that rethinking and readjusting were going on. We saw how good life can be in a world in which God has all things in control and where we could live fully and joyfully in harmony with the natural creation and ourselves … By repeatedly refusing to lay down laws for us, and patiently reiterating basic principles, the speakers gave useful guidelines.
> (Eggo, 1970, 7–8)

The participants too contributed to stimulating ideas and widening vision. On most days, at the first and last sessions, there were reports and prayer requests from the various countries.

> There was a new sense of urgency about them; a consciousness that the politics, economics and ideologies of this world are affecting us closely and demand our thoughtful attention … Emphasis was placed on the need for Christian nurses to achieve senior

positions in the profession in order to act as 'light' and 'salt' in the future pattern of nursing ... We heard how God is working where individuals are prepared to pray and work, to use imagination and courage to stand against wrong, and to give a positive lead by example and word.
(Eggo, 1970, 8)

During the 1970 conference, there were representatives from the USA for the first time and, instead of Katie James being the sole delegate from India (as had been the case at some previous conferences), there were now several attendees from India and Pakistan. The Swiss group's decorated wooden spoons sold well, as did the NCFI cookbook, Weighs and Means, which contained 150 recipes from 24 countries, all adding to the funds needed for outreach to other nurses.

The four-day leadership course, where 35 members gathered from 11 countries, had been a good preparation for a challenging conference, as well as for later work. One participant reported,

If we expected a package marked 'Leadership' we were in for a disappointment! Being honest with ourselves, others and God is difficult for most of us: it demands continuous and maturing learning of Christ, living in His light so that we can be what He wants us to be. Our morning sessions dealt with the application of these principles in professional and spiritual leadership ... An atmosphere of informality and purposefulness developed ... as we learned of the need to care for ourselves. Only then shall we be those who care for people and become leaders. Clarification of NCFI objectives and the training of leaders to achieve them were vital issues for our workshops.
(Lovett, 1970, 11)

At the General Committee meeting held after the conference, the new seven-strong Executive Committee was elected, including an American member, Miss Grace Wallace, for the first time. Johan Allan remained as President. It was also decided to have an International Council of Reference (a group of well-known Christians willing and able to give wise advice if NCFI referred a matter to them) and member countries were asked for nominations for this.

THE FIRST NCFI REGIONAL CONFERENCE

The very successful conference in St Andrews was not the only one for NCFI in 1970. In October the first Regional NCFI Conference for East Asia and Pacific, was held in Singapore and was attended by 30 delegates from 12 countries in the region: Australia, New Zealand, Fiji, Singapore (who were member countries) and Philippines, Malaysia, Japan, Korea, Indonesia, Papua New Guinea, Brunei and South Vietnam (Wyber, 1971, 6–10, 16). There was also first-hand news of the British Solomon Islands from a New Zealand nurse who had just visited.

This had been planned as a small conference with representatives from countries with NNCFs and at least one from Japan, Korea, Indonesia, Thailand, Laos and Taiwan. Travel was expensive, but plans had been made at the 1969 Executive Committee to distribute passport-sized photos of representatives from countries where there was no NNCF, to encourage people to 'adopt' them for sponsorship to the conference. Some delegates had faced problems before the conference, such as obtaining leave for the conference time, sickness, lack of travel funds, language barriers, and feelings of inadequacy. But once there they enjoyed the sharing of news and prayer requests, the Bible studies led by Bishop Chandu Ray, and the practical sessions – on how to lead Bible studies, how to run a hospital NCF, and on how to improve communication – led by Australian staff workers, Margaret Hutchison and Rae Argus. It was also a time for singing, getting to know each other, and for praying, not only for countries represented, but also the eight in the region which were not represented: Hong Kong (which had some autonomous groups), Taiwan (where some meetings had been held in mission hospitals), Burma (which was rather isolated, but which had had a small NCF for seven years), Laos, Cambodia, Thailand and New Hebrides. A nursing sister from Fiji was working in New Hebrides and also was interested in helping nurses in the Gilbert and Ellis Islands.

Despite geographical distances, financial and other challenges, this ANZEA conference – in what was later to be called the Pacific and East Asia (PACEA) Region – had demonstrated the benefits of a functional region within NCFI. The participants defined these benefits as:

- we are neighbours and a vital prayer partnership can be established because news can be readily circulated
- there is strength and encouragement in belonging to the wider Fellowship
- a region makes NCFI more realistic because NCFI then becomes people rather than names and places
- a regional conference is possible and rewarding
- it helps to unite the national Fellowship by pin-pointing its place in the international scene
- it promotes missionary vision, encouraging outreach on the scriptural principle of the early church
- problems can be shared, ideas interchanged , mistakes avoided and each other's burdens borne, because we care enough to help (Wyber, 1971, 10)

THE 1972 NCFI CONFERENCE, AND ICN MEXICO 1973

At the 1970 Executive Committee Meetings, it was decided that the world conference for NCFI should be held every four years, so that it would never be in the same year as the ICN Congress (which was held every four years), or other such events. As such, it was decided to hold the next Conference in 1972 to avoid a six-year gap, or a clash in 1973.

The 1972 NCFI Conference was held in Reuti Hasliberg, Switzerland, and was preceded by the now traditional leadership course – for 4 days 54 nurses from 16 nations and 5 continents followed the theme 'Living and serving together', with topics such as prayer and work, group dynamics, communicating, listening, starting a group, the generation gap, resources, spiritual renewal and sharing.

Then from 17–24 June 1972 the main conference on 'The whole man, in sickness and in health' was shared by participants from twenty-seven countries. By this time the Executive Committee included members from four continents, though each member was still elected as an individual, rather than representing a country or region.

Again the conference was in a beautiful place, a Christian hotel in the peace of countryside with colourful wild flowers, the sounds of waterfalls and cowbells, and views of snow-capped mountains. The traditional opening ceremony and presentation of flags by country representatives included a welcome for the three new member countries, Austria, India and the Philippines. The conference began with a service of Holy Communion, and continued with local and international music, morning prayer for different areas of the world, devotional and professional sessions, workshops, discussions and reports which helped to 'comfort the disturbed and disturb the comfortable'. At the closing meeting monetary thank offerings were collected from participants by five nurses, one from each continent, and Dr Agathe Burki offered these to God 'from all the world to all the world' (Klemet & Allan, 1972, 5–8).

There was insufficient representation to hold a General Committee Meeting that year, but an Executive Committee meeting was held immediately after the conference. At this meeting, evaluation comments on the leadership course and conference were discussed and, while reviews of the conference itself were favourable, it was revealed that many attendees considered the leadership course to have been too full. So it was decided that leaders' courses should be held at regional level every four years instead, between the main NCFI conferences. The PACEA region was already well defined – Blanche Lindsay was working part-time as co-ordinator for the region, communicating with nurses (some of them expatriate missionaries) in twelve countries – and so the NCFI Executive Committee discussed formation of a Regional Committee, and the degree of autonomy it should have, but there was no decision. However a PACEA Leaders' Course would be held every four years, and it was agreed that there should be one in America (including Latin America), and one in Europe which could include people from Africa and India, even though the other regions were not yet so well defined.

That year, the Committee approved Nigeria's application for NCFI membership, and four more individual members, and also agreed to contact people nominated by countries for the International Council of Reference. The draft of a membership certificate was approved for printing. It was agreed that travel was essential to communicate personally the vision of NCFI, and to do follow-up visits when possible, but 1974 should be left for possible regional conferences, unless there were other invitations.

Florence Yeboah (Ghana) expressed the need for leadership training in West Africa, and it was agreed that, when there was an organisational reason for a visit, Miss Allan should go and, when the visit was for leadership training, Dr Burki should go. So it was agreed that Dr Burki would try to visit West Africa soon.

Staff for the future was an important issue raised at this meeting. Johan Allan had expressed her desire to retire from the Secretary's post she had held 'temporarily' since 1969, and it was clear that her replacement would need another member of staff to help with the office work. It was difficult to communicate adequately without help, but also recipients did not always answer letters, and news for prayer letters was lacking sometimes. It was agreed that the next prayer letter would include a request for prayer for a General Secretary – the aim would be to interest potential applicants perhaps at the ICN or regional conferences – and that someone be appointed to the position before 1976. An office secretary would be employed and new office space sought for NCFI since the current space would be inadequate for two people, though it was agreed that sharing with the national NCF would not be possible as it was important to keep the two organisations separate. These necessary decisions were taken in faith, to meet the needs of the growing organisation.

The Committee were thankful to God for the healthy state of NCFI finances, the needs having increased with NCFI now having three staff – with Johan Allan remaining as Secretary until a suitable replacement was found, Blanche Lindsay the part-time PACEA co-ordinator, and Lois Cumming in Argentina (with joint support from her mission society).

Finally, the Executive Committee discussed plans for various NCFI events to be held at the ICN Congress in Mexico in 1973, building on the good experience and many contacts from 1965 and 1969. An ad hoc committee in the USA had already been working on this, and one member had visited Miss Margarethe Kruse, President of ICN, who had also identified herself with NCF Denmark. It was agreed that the successful Friendship Lounge was to be a feature and that the NCFI leaflet should be made available in the four official languages of the ICN, English, French, German and Spanish, while nurses involved in NCFI would be encouraged to use their various languages while helping in the lounge and events.

The ICN Congress in Mexico City in 1973 proved to be a busy and exciting week with many opportunities for the people who came, though physical exertion at that altitude provided challenges for those unused to it. At the NCFI booth, from 8.30 a.m. to 7 p.m., relays of five people (two Spanish-speaking) talked with visitors about Nurses Christian Fellowships in their part of the world and about NCFI. By the end of the week a wealth of NCFI literature and nearly 3,000 New Testaments (2,100 in Spanish, 600 English and several more in French) had been given away, and more than 200 people had asked for information about the NCFs in their own country (Rosti, 1973, 5).

At the evening meeting in a nearby hotel, 150 (from 23 of the 74 countries with delegates at the Congress) listened as Johan Allan gave a talk on 'Spiritual Resources for the Nurse'. Many Mexican nurses had attended and the company was so lively that the socialising after the talk continued for some time. As one person commented, 'When God gives a party He really does a good job!'

At least two groups planned to meet and to reach out to others after the congress, and nurses from Peru, Ecuador and Argentina met to consider how they might reach out in their own countries. The effects of contact with NCFI on many others may never be known.

In 1974 a conference was held in Austria for the European Region (though it had not yet been developed as an NCFI Region by the countries within it) and, by chance, all continents in NCFI were represented. So, since no General Committee meeting had been held at the 1972 NCFI conference (due to the insufficient number of member countries represented), it was decided to hold an ad hoc General Committee at the regional conference instead. Here, NCFI began to plan for the 1976 conference which was to be held in Ghana. The Executive Committee which followed the conference discussed this further.

CHANGES AND PROGRESS – A GENERAL DIRECTOR FOR NCFI

The year 1975 was significant because of several new developments, including the appointment of Ruth Lichtenberger as the new General Secretary or, as the role was now named, General Director. Ruth was an American graduate nurse, who had worked for a number of years as a staff member of the national NCF. She had long felt called by God to mission work and had prepared for it, but had not felt called to work in any particular country. With her appointment to NCFI staff she would be based in another country (England) and work in many different countries. The Executive Committee discussed the draft job description for the General Director further, and accepted the offer from the USA to second Ruth with current salary and pension for three years. As Johan Allan had accepted a minimal salary, and NCFI expenses would now rise, the offer was a major contribution and had been intended no matter who was appointed. Johan Allan remained as President but handed over as Secretary to the new General Director in July 1975, working with Ruth (who was also assisted by an office secretary, Beryl Stewart, another American nurse) until September.

But there were other personnel changes at the 1975 Executive Committee meeting that May. Dr Agathe Burki, who had always supported NCF Switzerland and who had been involved in leadership in NCFI since its beginnings, resigned from the Committee. As a young Hungarian medical student she had been involved in Inter-Varsity Fellowship (IVF) in Zurich, and in around 1950 they began to help nurses to start Bible study groups in hospitals, and then to form a national NCF. She was a lively and gifted speaker with a strong character. She had an active part to play at the NCFI Conference in Switzerland in 1958, and her commitment to the work was such that, despite her advanced state of pregnancy, play it she did. On the last night she went off on the back of her husband's motorbike, and it was not long before news was received of the birth of their fourth child. (*Highway* No. 56, 1975/3, 5)

She had made a particular contribution to NCFI over the years –

providing leadership courses for nurses, speaking at conferences, doing other committee work and, during travel for other purposes, making visits to encourage and inform nurses (and others interested in Christian work amongst nurses) about NCFI. She was known and valued by nurses in many parts of the world. As she had changed to different work and was no longer involved in NCF she resigned, but agreed to join the NCFI Council of Reference.

That same year Florence Yeboah, from NCF Ghana and another non-nurse, announced that she too wanted to resign from the Executive Committee, of which she had been a part since 1969. She had believed the role would be better suited to a Ghanaian nurse, but agreed to wait until the NCFI Conference and General Committee in Ghana in 1976 before relinquishing her role. Under God's guidance, leadership of NCFI would then be entirely in the hands of nurses.

Two new members were then co-opted to the Committee, Evangeline Creighton of Scotland and Grete Scharfe of Denmark. Both were destined for long-term involvement and valuable work with NCFI.

The matter of personnel changes now resolved, attention turned to the status of member countries. NCF Switzerland had ceased activity, and since there had been very little contact with France, Portugal and Trinidad and Tobago, it was decided to ask if they wished to continue their associate membership – they unfortunately withdrew.

The news was not all negative, however. In many parts of the world – especially in fledgling member countries where NCFs were active even if small – work was initiated and/or supported through expatriate missionary nurses, and this sometimes led to full-time NCF work. Grace Stokes, an English missionary, had been seconded by her mission to work full-time with FCN (NCF Nigeria) and there was news of developing work in eleven other countries. These included Ecuador and Japan, where Nancy Larson (missionary to Ecuador) and Jean Webber and Barbara Dicks (missionaries to Japan) had been seconded to work with nurses by their respective mission societies. Nancy Larsen had visited Colombia and found ten Professors of Nursing meeting weekly for Bible study and prayer. But always, of course, the aim was to develop leaders from the country itself.

Continuing professional development and involvement of NNCFs was evident in, for example, the 'Persons in Crisis' workshops in the USA, Australia and New Zealand; a spiritual care workshop in Denmark; a new NCF Professional Development Committee in England; and attendance at the PanAmerican Congress by some of those working with NCFI in Latin America.

In many countries NCF had been seen as a means of maintaining Christian commitment and fellowship for nurses who lived in hospital accommodation, and were often unable to attend church because of their work and shift systems. This was beginning to change as increasingly nurses were married and/or lived in their own homes, and had more off duty time. But the role of NCF in helping nurses to develop professionally as Christian nurses was increasingly being recognised in many countries, and NCFI with its worldwide contacts and resources of people (if not always finance) had already begun to fulfil its role in supporting this.

Sometimes the spread of knowledge and ideas was through conference sessions or international committees, and sometimes in other ways. For example material from the English NCF Summer Schools, designed to help young people still at school to learn more about nursing and Christian faith and life, was used by the Danish Fellowship to start similar events. This led to more young Christians who became involved in the Fellowship as they came into nursing and, developing as leaders, they changed the nature of the Fellowship. Fifteen years after the collapse of the Danish Fellowship in 1961 it became an NCFI member. (Bollerud, 1976, 8–9)

Resources were/are always a relevant consideration in NCFI work, in that frequently needs and opportunities are more evident than sources of money and other necessities to meet them. God has endless resources, but sometimes these must be worked for or found by humans.

NCFI had some problems with resources because it was international (as well as because of nurses' low salaries), but often these could be overcome. For example, it was difficult to send money out of Ghana, but Ghanaian nurses in the UK were providing Ghana's contributions to NCFI and sending in the Ghanaian subscriptions for *Highway*. In other places where it could not be sent out, money for NCFI was kept in the country and used for NCFI purposes such as conferences or visits from abroad by NCFI staff or committee members.

THE 1976 CONFERENCE – NCFI IN AFRICA

From its early days NCFI had had contacts in Africa, often either expatriate missionary nurses, or African nurses who had trained in Europe and returned home. NCF work by nationals had been growing, particularly in Ghana and Nigeria and in 1976 the NCFI Conference was held outside Europe for the first time, in Ghana.

The theme of the ninth International Conference, held from 3–16 August 1976 in the University of Ghana, Legon, was 'The Unchangeableness of God', an appropriate theme for many reasons. In some ways the conference was similar to others, with the Chief Nursing Officer for Ghana and other officials, as well as NCF/NCFI leaders, taking part in the Opening Ceremony – where representatives of the 25 countries to which the 187 participants belonged each carried in their flag during the roll-call procession. There were morning sessions of Bible-teaching by the Revd Canon Olajide of the University of Ife, Nigeria, and professional plenary and workshop sessions led by nurses. There were prayer times, and of course informal times of recreation and fellowship, but the physical and cultural environment was very different.

The natural and human sounds and vivid colours of Africa, the food and facilities – all were new to many of the visiting nurses, and the fascinating rhythms of clapping, and dancing during worship were a new experience for many. During the day excursion by bus to the beautiful palm-fringed beach and huge dam, conferees enjoyed time talking together informally and perhaps singing one of the two Ghanaian conference songs everyone learned, while watching from the buses the villages, crowded markets, foods sold by the road side, and beautiful children everywhere.

However the unchangeable love and power of God, reflected in

His people, was the major experience, as the following testimonies show.

> Each evening slides and reports from various countries revealed to me the difficulties and joys my Christian brothers and sisters are facing around the world ... Yet it is wonderfully encouraging to hear how God is raising up NCF groups in Africa, and that in the Philippines there are many NCF groups starting in nursing schools ... Nothing can compare with this experience which really strengthened my faith in God and reminded me that NCFI is His doing and He is actively at work in nurses' lives world-wide. My intercessory prayer life should deepen as a result of my increased awareness of needs.
> *Gloria Larson*
> (Fish, 1976, 13)

> Our first impression of Ghana was the overwhelming welcome and hospitality. The uninhibited freedom in worship, leadership and evangelism of our African friends has certainly been a lesson to us. To experience the oneness in fellowship despite the differences in culture and background has been a tremendous joy.
> *Some Australian impressions*

> This conference has been a real thrilling experience in my life. We have represented many countries yet one profession, but from different cultures and backgrounds. We have seen the harmony of living together and mutual love because of our faith in the Lord Jesus ... It has broadened my outlook on God's work among nurses and has challenged my heart to fulfil the many lessons I have learned in this conference in my own life, in my Fellowship and regions around Malaysia.
> *Oi Poh Choo*
> (*Highway* No. 61, 1976/4, 14–15)

Again there was intellectual and professional as well as spiritual challenge:

Even though some lectures were hard to understand, there were some which were very useful to me and I can share with my Thai friends in London.
Sue Banyotooey – Thailand
(*Highway* No. 61, 1976/4, 14–15)

It was not only language which was a challenge sometimes, but professional concepts such as the nursing process (systematic individualised nursing care) which were taught by Barbara Simsen (an Australian staff worker) and other speakers, and which related to spiritual care of patients. Such concepts were new or relatively new in both western and other parts of the world. The quotations above summarise and bring to life some of the ways in which this conference and others fulfilled some of the aims of NCFI, maintaining the essential Christian spiritual aspects while changing to meet the needs of Christian nurses in a changing professional nursing environment.

THE END OF AN ERA – JOHAN ALLAN'S RETIREMENT

One major change for NCFI in 1976 was the retirement of Johan Allan. She had been elected President in 1958 and re-elected five times, serving for a total of eighteen years and had also served as General Secretary (with a minimal salary) for almost seven years, before handing over to Ruth Lichtenberger.

Although it is not possible in this history to do justice to all those who have served in NCFI, it is fitting to consider how God prepared Johan for the great service she gave to NCFI, leading and helping to sustain it through its formative years (based on a tribute in *Highway* No. 61, 1976/4, 6–7).

Johan Allan was born in 1911 and brought up in a small Scottish village, and went to London to train as a State Registered Fever Nurse and General Nurse and a State Certified Midwife. She spent five years working at the King George V Hospital in Malta, mostly during the Second World War, when the island was bombed a great deal. She then returned to Scotland and worked in various posts for nine years.

During her spare time she acted as Honorary Secretary for the Scottish NCF, and also started to correspond with nurses in a number of countries. Then she was invited to return as matron to the hospital in Malta, which was threatened with closure due to debt. She did so and saw that the only solution was to invite the staff to work on a faith basis, paying the bills first, and accepting as personal allowances equal shares of what remained up to a small maximum. Anything remaining was put into the funds of the hospital, which gradually became financially sound. She remained there for ten years as matron and, as Malta was a small island in the line of many trade routes, people of many nationalities passed through and were sometimes patients.

In 1961 she returned to the UK and worked professionally at the General Nursing Council in London until she retired at 59 to take on the full-time work of NCFI General Secretary. Again she accepted only a minimal salary, alongside her small pension, and was generously supported with accommodation and overhead expenses, sharing a London home with Betty Kettle – a friend who held a very senior nursing post in England, a member of NCFI Executive Committee for many years, and editor of *Highway*, the NCFI news and prayer publication.

With God's help Johan Allan had steered NCFI through some difficult times, such as the 1967 separation from the newly formed Hospital Christian Fellowship International; had travelled to many parts of the world (often at her own expense or with the assistance of friends); had established firmly the role of NCFI within professional nursing contexts such as the International Council of Nursing Conferences; and helped NCFI to grow to include twenty member countries as well as nurse contacts in many other countries.

She had a strong character but was physically small, quiet and unassuming – a leader full of 'sanctified commonsense' who enabled others to fulfil their potential. Letters written to her by people in sixteen countries who had heard about her retirement in 1976 mention 'her example, wisdom, graciousness, energy, loving concern, friendship, prayerful perseverance, caring concern, sacrifice, unstinting efforts, of being a wonderful communicator, of her leadership and courage' (*Highway* No. 61, 1976/4, 6).

At the 1976 General Committee, after a prayer for guidance in choosing the new President, Johan made the following comments on the role (there were at that time no men with the necessary experience of NCFI to make them eligible for the post):

- She should be a woman of God, called by God to this position.
- She should have a certain amount of business acumen.
- She should be an administrator and organizer.
- Her thinking should be universal and not insular.
- She should be acceptable to the nursing profession in her own country and at international level.
- She should be able to understand and appreciate the wide variety of patterns that exist among Nurses' Christian Fellowships.
- At this early stage in the General Director's career, it was advisable that she be readily available for consultation.
- We should remember that men look on the outward appearance, but God looks on the heart.
(General Committee Minutes, 1976, 2–3)

These comments were obviously based on her many years of experience of fulfilling these criteria; which in turn was evidently based on God's preparation of her for her NCFI roles and her continued dependence on Him.

The 1976 General Committee invited her to remain a lifetime *ex officio* member of the Executive Committee; an offer she accepted, and so remained a wise advisor to NCFI as long as age and health permitted. Probably her last NCFI event before her death in 1997 was a short visit in 1990 with Betty Kettle to the European Regional Conference in Pitlochry, Scotland, not too far from her home in the little village of St Monans. For old friends it was a joy to see her again, and for a new generation in NCFI it was an encounter with history. Many people have thanked God, and sometimes still do so, for the great gift of Johan Allan and all that she contributed to and through NCFI from its beginning, and for those who supported her in this work in various ways.

4

1976–1988: A NEW ERA AND INCREASING REGIONALISATION

THE 1976 COMMITTEE MEETINGS – DECISIONS FOR THE FUTURE

The General Committee met during the 1976 conference in Ghana to accomplish its first task, the election, so that the new Executive Committee and President could be presented to conference participants before they went home. Delegates of thirteen member countries were present, but Austria, Fiji, Israel, Singapore and Spain were not represented. There were observers from seven additional countries, including Zambia (Zambia's new staff worker had not had opportunity to be briefed as a delegate by the Zambian Committee).

Of the previous Executive Committee members 3 had resigned, 3 were elected and 2 co-opted members were re-elected together with 4 new members, and later 2 more new members were co-opted. The new Executive Committee was the largest so far. The eleven members were still elected as individuals, on the basis of their professional nursing and NCF/NCFI experience and qualifications, rather than as representatives of any area. But for the first time all were nurses, and they included people from Africa, America, Europe and the PACEA region. Grace Wallace, Director of NCF USA and a member of the previous Executive Committee, was elected to be the new President, and Blanche Lindsay of Australia was re-elected as Vice-President.

After a long, often busy, but enjoyable conference time, the General Committee met for two days, to be followed by two days of Executive Committee meetings – the Lord gives strength! As the last full General Committee had been held in 1970 (with only an ad hoc meeting held at the European Conference in 1974 to plan for the NCFI Conference in Ghana), Johan Allan took the opportunity to review major events in NCFI during this time, while also orienting the new delegates.

She spoke about the move NCFI had made from Glasgow to London in 1969 and her own resignation as President in 1975. She mentioned the appointment of Ruth Lichtenberger as General Director later that same year, paying tribute to Ruth's gifts and experience, and the way in which she had adapted to 'a new job, a new country, and a new way of life'. She discussed the reprinting (with agreed changes) of the NCFI Constitution in 1967, the formation of the International Council of Reference and the distribution of certificates of membership to each NCFI member country, both of which had taken place in 1972.

Regionalisation was a major topic for discussion at this meeting. The PACEA Region, spearheaded by Blanche Lindsay in 1968, had already had two successful Regional Conferences – the first held in Singapore in 1970 and the second in Penang, Malaysia in 1974 where a four-strong committee, including Blanche Lindsay as co-ordinator, were appointed. Blanche was unable to attend the 1976 conference and General Committee meeting, but she sent a detailed letter in which she recommended that NCF staff workers in the region should also be able to attend Regional Committee meetings, and that ideally the Regional Co-ordinator should be a full-time worker. Delegates present from the six countries of the PACEA Region (which at that time included India and Pakistan) were asked for their comments on the benefits of regionalisation. They outlined these as:

- Closer affinity with and concern for countries in the Region
- Circulation of detailed news and prayer items
- Being valuable for small groups of mixed cultures
- Being the only way to get the countries together

Though asked, they offered no comments on disadvantages, and the presence of so many countries' delegates suggested that regionalisation had encouraged rather than discouraged involvement in the wider international arena. It seemed that there was much to recommend it, with each country feeling a greater need to be involved with, and have concern for, countries where no NCF existed. Considering the formation of other regions, the Chairman said that regionalisation began with a person, a person with a vision and the initiative to put it into practice.

Two other issues related to the regional experience were discussed: the advisability of having regional newsletters or magazines; and regional finance. A more localised publication gave good coverage for local news and needs, and therefore was a stimulant for prayer; but there was overlap with the content of *Highway*, the NCFI magazine, and it was not always wise to circulate personal or sensitive matters. A solution agreed by consensus was that *Highway* should have world coverage, and each region would prepare and insert a supplement of more localised news and prayer requests. It was noted that countries seemed unaware that others would be interested in their news, and often failed to send it.

As regards finance, based on the PACEA experience it was recommended that regional finances be obtained and retained within the region, as it seemed to stimulate more giving, and regular financial statements should be sent to the region's member countries. It was also recommended that NCFI should receive a copy of these statements, and a percentage of the regional funds should be sent regularly to NCFI Headquarters, in addition to individual countries' commitments to NCFI. Financial affairs tend to be complicated in international organisations and, for currency exchange rate reasons, no money had been sent (by agreement) from PACEA to NCFI in 1974–5, but quite a large amount was sent on request in 1976.

It was evident that if regionalisation was to move forward successfully more detailed plans were necessary and, as requested, the Executive Committee which met after the General Committee worked on guidelines for regions. These included the purposes of regionalisation.

Fellowships within a region are:
1) To help each other to fulfil the purposes of NCFI
2) To provide facilities for training in leadership
3) To support smaller member Fellowships
4) To assist developing countries to begin NNCFs

A key nurse for the region was thought to be essential, even if not a full-time worker, and it was decided that regional work should be based on established NNCFs. It was recommended that a period of work under the guidance of a Caretaker Committee should be reviewed before election of an official Regional Committee, which should consist of the co-ordinator and three others, at least three of the committee being nurses.

Organisationally, regions would not be an additional administrative layer between NCFI Headquarters and NNCFs, who would still have direct access to the General Director. The General Committee, comprising delegates of member countries, remained the policy-making body for NCFI. The Regional Committees would each be responsible for briefing two delegates of their member countries to bring regional thinking to the General Committee.

People were obviously the most important resource in developing both NNCFs and regions, and at this time NCFI began a period of increase in the number of NNCF staff seconded by missions, and an additional staff member for NCFI in general. Jean Webber and Barbara Dicks (of OMF) were already working in Japan and Nancy Larson was still working in Ecuador, seconded by World Radio Missionary Fellowship and financed by her home church. But since the last General Committee meeting several more missionaries had begun to work with NCFI – Margaret Corin (New Zealand, who later, in 1986, was appointed to NCFI staff and was then paid and employed/managed by NCFI) had joined Nancy in Ecuador; Gaye Mercier (Australia) had now offered for Peru, seconded by the Australian Church Mission Society to work with NCFI; and Fiona Ross (England) had offered for Argentina, with full support initially from The Evangelical Alliance Relief (TEAR) Fund to work with NCFI.

In addition, the Fellowship had acquired a new NCFI staff member, Barbara Simsen (Australia). Barbara had originally been suggested as a worker for PACEA, but it emerged at the General Committee that her skills, which included an ability to lead groups with themes such as 'People in Crisis' or 'Love that Heals', were considered better fitted for work with established NNCFs, rather than a regional co-ordinator's role. She was appointed as an NCFI staff worker, with a brief for education and development of educational materials; and she later edited *Christian Nurse International* – a more professional successor to *Highway* – as well as activities such as conference planning and materials and deputising for the General Director during her study leave.

NCFI was clearly becoming big enough to require more complex administrative arrangements, and the skills of the new President and Executive Committee – gained in NCF and professional nursing experience and education – were well used in matters such as developing job descriptions, procedure for appointment and contracts for the new regional co-ordinators and NCFI staff members. But their skills were also utilised in reviewing the budget and evaluation responses from the conference, in planning for the next ICN Congress in Japan in 1977, and in recognising that a more efficient method of decision-making was necessary – the Executive Committee needed a little aid in accomplishing its duties.

Recognising the larger number and wide geographical dispersion of the Executive Committee members, a Standing Committee of six of these was set up to act as necessary. At a time when fax and email were not yet available, and postal and telephone communication could take time and be uncertain in some countries, this was often very necessary. Although it was expected that each Executive Committee member would attend at least two of its meetings every four years, this was not easy, given the cost of travel – even though these were timed when possible to be immediately before or after other conferences. For example, in addition to staff, there were 4 members at the 1978 Executive Meeting, and 5 in 1979, but of these members only the President was present at both meetings. Most members still paid personally for their travel, but from the time when the committee grew to twelve members, and came from more countries, there were always some whose attendance depended on sponsorship from NCFI or others. It is not easy for very different individuals from different countries, nursing and cultural backgrounds, and varied experience in committee work, to come together and work intensively and productively for just a few days once a year or less, trying to address great challenges around the world with relatively small apparent financial resources. Yet this is what members at the NCFI Executive and General Committee meetings (and the succeeding bodies) have done.

That God's work through NCFI has continued to grow and develop through many years despite such challenges is due to His power and also the faith, work and prayers not only of those at the committees, but also those who have supported them in various ways.

THE NEXT TWELVE YEARS – LANDMARKS AND REGIONALISATION

At the previous ICN Congress, held in 1973 in Mexico City, NCFI had been advised on the need to prepare the following for the 1977 Congress:

1) materials related to the profession and culturally oriented in several languages
2) writers for articles conceptually related to the profession
3) committed Christians able to speak forthrightly in professional organisations and the congress
4) Christian nurses to determine individually and collectively the Christian position on large national issues i.e. abortion, nursing ethics.

(Rosti, 1973, 5–7)

In 1977 the ICN Congress was held in Japan, the largest international convention yet held there. In a country with about 1 per cent Christians in the population it was not easy to arrange NCFI participation, and as usual there were some organisational difficulties when the time arrived. But as usual the Lord was in control. The 15 Japanese nurses, 20 missionaries and 5 'ICN foreigners' (non-Japanese Christian nurses, probably members of NNCFs who were there to attend the ICN Congress) who helped at the booth in the exhibition at various times were all kept busy.

By closing time 400 Spanish, 1,600 English and 4,000 Japanese Gideon New Testaments, 200 Japanese Living New Testaments, 300 each of French and German 'Marks', plus 8,000 JBS [possibly Japanese Bible Society] pamphlets had been received willingly, and many names and addresses recorded of those who wished to have New Testaments sent … Some delegates asked to be given the surplus literature in their particular languages.
(*Highway* No. 65, 1977/4, 4–5)

This literature, and copies of the NCFI magazines available, went out to delegates from eighty-nine countries, with the prayers of those who gave it.

At the open NCFI meeting, 280 nurses enjoyed the fellowship of nurses from many different nations and had the pleasure of hearing two speakers, Dr Masume Toyotome and Dr Virginia Ohlson – an American nurse already well known in Japan where she had been sent by her country to help after the Second World War. The impact on the lives of all those present cannot be known, but no doubt it was a learning experience for nurse Chieko Fukushima. She had temporarily left her studies in the USA to help during the 1977 ICN Congress, and would later spend many years as the first Japanese staff worker for the country's developing NNCF, building, as happened in many countries, on the pioneering work of expatriate missionaries.

Like its members, NCFI continued to develop and grow. In 1978 the Fellowship was able, for the first time, to provide a witness at the International Council of Midwives Conference, held that year in Israel; while 1980 marked the tenth NCFI Conference, held in Kolding, Denmark.

Hosting the conference was an act of faith by the Danish NNCF, which had only about 195 members, but it proved to be of real benefit to them, as well as to participants from other countries. One of the items in the conference pack was a small leaflet prepared by some of the Danish nurses, which gave a brief account of the geography, social welfare and customs, and other aspects of Denmark, and which was very helpful for many nurses from very distant and different parts of the world.

The main speakers addressing the theme of 'The Christian Nurse in a Secular Society' were Baroness Jean McFarlane, a well-known Professor of Nursing from England, and Revd Michael Wilcox, a theologian. Both of them used, as the main Biblical basis for their talks, the Book of Nehemiah, particularly the sections about the rebuilding of the ruined walls of Jerusalem when the Jews returned from exile. This had been requested by the conference organisers.

There were approximately 300 nurses from 26 or more countries in attendance, and while they all varied in education, experience and the context in which they nursed, it was evident in the lively reports and prayer, and from interaction in small groups and informal contact, that they faced many similar challenges, as well as some different ones. There was much to learn from each other, in workshops and through conversations during the enjoyable meals, outings and other activities. Workshops available included both specifically 'Christian life' topics, such as 'Bible study'; 'Productive Prayer'; 'Witness with Wisdom'; 'Tips or Tithes'; and 'How to Start an NNCF'. But there were also more 'professional' topics to discuss, such as 'Publish or Perish'; 'Life and Death Matters' (where the practices of abortion and euthanasia were discussed); 'In Search of Spiritual Need'; 'Rights and Responsibilities' (where attendees debated whether Christians should join unions and go on strike); and 'Caring for the Carers'.

The school facilities provided space for NCFI and various NNCFs' displays, and there was also a gift stall, full of crafts and conference souvenirs, from which the proceeds would go to NCFI. There was translation with earphones for the main language groups. When the rain eventually stopped, the extensive grounds and the lake provided a lovely area for the Danish dancing, for walks and for the conference photograph. Even the rain received some credit for contributing to the green countryside and productive farms which were spotted on the excursion, as well as the view of Sky Mountain, which stands at an impressive 400 feet above the flat Danish landscape.

Meals provided more than just enjoyment – at one meal people sat at tables labelled according to their region; at another they joined tables organised according to nursing interest (for example nursing education, management or other specialities) which was a useful way of sharing ideas and getting to know others with common interests.

The evening Regional Sharing sessions on Europe, Africa, Americas and Pacific and East Asia also promoted a sense of regional identity, though India and some of its neighbouring countries were beginning to consider whether they should have a separate region, given that PACEA covered such a wide geographical area.

Betty Kettle – who had been closely involved in NCFI almost since the beginning, as an Executive Committee member, as editor of *Highway* from 1969–78, and in countless other ways – presented the evening session entitled 'The Spotlight on NCFI', which marked the twenty-fifth year since a group of nurses at Keswick first met in

1956 to discuss the possibility of forming such an organisation. As part of this session she gave a brief history of stages of development of NCFI, under the title 'Built and Building Together', ending with three ways in which an NNCF may start in relation to NCFI, and the verse, 'Except the Lord build the house, they labour in vain that build it' (Psalm 127.1).

Building, a key theme for the main conference speakers, was reflected in the Nehemiah Bible study booklets, the printed guides for use during the programmed daily Quiet Times (such a time for prayer and Bible-reading is part of the daily routine of many Christians wherever they are), and in Cornerstones, a daily A4 sheet, which provided conference news in English and Danish. The Bible study booklets would later contribute to literature available from NCFI.

There was also the launch of Project Nehemiah, through which people were invited to buy 'bricks' and so contribute to the purchase and renovation of a house in Penge, a London suburb, to provide a new home for NCFI Headquarters. One small office was now insufficient for NCFI's needs, and it was hoped that this purchase, with the help of a low-cost loan, would both save rent and provide more facilities and accommodation. Apart from the professional work done in renovation, many hours of energy-consuming voluntary work on the building were to be contributed by the NCFI staff and visitors from various parts of the world during the next few years, while those nurses who could not visit in person, would offer support through prayer and finance. NCFI's new 'home' was completed in 1982.

In addition to the new location there were other changes in NCFI discussed by the 1980 General Committee. Blanche Lindsay – who had served faithfully and contributed so much as Vice-President since her election in 1967, as well as being a key leader in the development of the first NCFI Region, PACEA in 1968 – resigned from the committee owing to new professional responsibilities. When the new Executive Committee were elected in 1980, Grace Wallace asked to relinquish her position as President, agreeing to stand for election as Vice-President in view of her increasing responsibilities as Director of NCF USA. The continued availability of her personal and organisational gifts and her experience was greatly valued in this office. Pat Ashworth, an

English nurse involved internationally for professional as well as NCFI reasons, was elected President.

In 1981, the seventeenth ICN Quadrennial Congress was held in Los Angeles and NCF USA had been working for many months on preparations to make the most of the occasion, which hosted 6,127 nurses from around 90 nations.

Each morning 35–40 nurses and students met at the Salvation Army Centre near the Convention Hall to share fellowship; to enjoy breakfasts provided and hosted by Los Angeles NCF groups; and to pray for nurse leaders and speakers involved in the Congress, some of them NCF members. At the NCFI stall at the congress many conferees were delighted to find someone who spoke their language (Spanish, Japanese, Danish, French, Portuguese and English), to learn about NNCFs and NCFI, to receive copies of Scripture available in thirteen languages, and perhaps to buy Bible Studies or a spiritual care book, available in three or four languages. (*Highway*, No. 80, 1981/3, 13–15)

It was a joy to meet leaders of national nursing organisations who identified themselves as Christians and, for the NCF members from ten countries who served at the stall, it was a joy to work together and learn from each other. At the NCFI Dinner, when Barbara Simsen spoke on 'Spiritual Care, the Essential Option', guests were challenged to think about questions like, Who am I? What am I here for? Where am I going?

This ICN Congress was significant internationally in the election of the first ICN President from a developing country, Kenya. No doubt it was also a significant time for many of those in contact with NCFI there.

The 1985 ICN Congress in Tel Aviv, Israel, was smaller, with around three thousand participants. One major impression was the extent of the efforts to cope with, care for and integrate the thousands of Jews arriving from many different countries into this small country – the Holy Land – yet evidently prepared in case of war.

Again helpers at the NCFI stall, from 8 countries, were kept busy talking to around 300 people per day. There were comments that the area was always crowded, and people did not just look and walk away, but stayed to talk and all left with some literature. Bibles were on sale (giving them was not allowed) and sales went so well that supplies ran short. With the congress on several sites, the best place for prayer and picnic lunch proved to be in shade under the trees outside the main congress centre. Out on the grass each day between 15 and 35 people enjoyed fellowship, fresh air, and shade from the hot sun, with approximately fifty people attending at least once.

Despite competition from many other events on the one 'free' evening of the congress, 150 people gathered to hear Baroness Jean McFarlane speak on 'Nurses – a force for what?', going on to discuss nurses as a force for caring, and a force for God. Once again the ICN Congress had proved to be one of NCFI's most useful outreach activities, despite the heavy financial cost (just over £3,000 on this occasion), with over one hundred follow-up cards which required further action.

A HISTORIC LANDMARK – INDIA, 1984

Every NCFI conference has similarities – in the quality of Bible teaching, the warmth of fellowship, and in the opportunities for personal, spiritual and professional learning and friendships, all in a unique multicultural environment, as nurses from many nations come together sharing their Christian faith and love of nursing. Each conference is also different, not least because of the various geographical and cultural locations in which they take place. But the eleventh NCFI World Conference, held in 1984 in New Delhi, India was to be historically unique.

At the 1980 conference, ENFI (the Indian NCF) had agreed, with some trepidation, to invite NCFI to hold the next conference in India. It seemed such a huge challenge and they were concerned they might not be able to offer the standard of facilities enjoyed in the West. But NCF members from many countries were eager to be there, and as ENFI began to plan and work for it, they realised that with God's help they could meet the challenges and host the conference.

The conference began on 28 October 1984 at the New Delhi YMCA, though a smaller group of nurses had met from 24–28 October for the NCFI Leadership Seminar. Then the other main conference participants arrived – 350 nurses and students from all over India and 29 other countries. The conference theme, 'Free to be Accountable', was addressed by the main speakers, Revd P.T. Chandapilla (who had originally trained as a nurse) and a number of nurses who spoke at the five professional plenary sessions and the many workshops. Before starting his sessions on the book of Galatians, Revd Chandapilla was asked to comment on his expectations of the conference. One expectation was, that 'our guests would experience some of the ethos and pathos of this country', and would use that experience to pray with insight into its needs. (*Highway* Vol. 1, No. 1, 1985, 18). He could not know how uniquely this would be fulfilled.

At the opening session a welcome message was read from Mrs Indira Gandhi, the Prime Minister of India and a leader respected not least for her insistence on freedom of religion. Three days later she was shot and died, and there was conflict, uproar and violence in India:

> Curfew, killings, ears glued to the radio, every newspaper purchased and thoroughly read. What does this mean for the conference programme? How do we, as visitors, grieve with our Indian colleagues? When meeting with YMCA and ENFI leaders we were informed that we were 'perfectly safe' to continue. Recognising the need for us all to grieve, a condolence meeting, time to watch the funeral on TV, and a prayer vigil were arranged. Both Indian and visiting conferees prayed for the Gandhi family and the nation. (*Highway* Vol. 1, No. 1, 1985, 18)

This brief record will no doubt bring to mind many more personal memories for the conference participants. The giving to each Indian participant of a single rose by a 'visitor' participant at the condolence service; the care and courage of the Indian hosts who kept conferees safe and well-fed, despite possible dangers in going out to buy food when there was unrest and violence in many parts of India; the way in which one workshop group, whose leader had to leave to go to an emergency meeting, happily proceeded with the interactive workshop, and were just finishing lively discussion when she returned at the finish time; the way in which people got to know each other more deeply, being unable to go out, and learned from people's different reactions (one example was a response to an enquiry as to how a group from a distant part of the world were coping – 'Oh they're fine. They say it's just like home!'). In the midst of 'visitors' concern for their worried families at home, there was much prayer and concern too for the Indian people and their families, perhaps affected by the violence in many parts of India, and for their safe travel home after the conference. Many of the 'visitors' had never before fully realised the huge size of the country, and the diversity of people, states and languages within it.

Despite the upheaval in the country, and views from the roof of disturbances in Delhi, the conference continued in the peace and colourful interior of the shamiana, a huge tent in the courtyard where the main meetings were held, and the various rooms of the YMCA. People had come to the conference for many different reasons, and experienced India at a historic time. Whatever their reasons for coming, all had contributed to it and many received 'far more than expected' according to their evaluation forms. Two comments received after return from the conference convey some of what that meant,

> I am still reflecting on all I learned and felt at the conference. I will never be the same! My world is larger, my circle of friends wider, my trust and faith in God greater ...
> *American delegate*

On Wednesday we had our regular ENFI group. We sang songs and choruses we learnt during the conference and promised to teach them. We are experiencing a sort of 'homesickness' after returning from Delhi. We feel that it was like heaven and we have met our own family members. I feel that God allowed us to have a little glimpse of His glorious Kingdom ... and left us imagining the beauty and joy of the eternal one. Please pray for me. I want to do the Bible studies on Galatians with the group here. Some of the students filled in ENFI membership forms after we shared our experiences with them. I told them that it is really wonderful to have a sense of belonging to a nationwide ... a worldwide family of

Christian nurses ... I am sure the Holy Spirit has already started
His work in their hearts.
Indian delegate
(*Highway* Vol. 1, No. 1, 1985, 19)

After the conference, delegates from 19 countries and observers
from 6 others met for the 2 days of General Committee meetings. Their
work included considering NCFI itself and how it should help NNCFs
in difficulties, accepting the revised constitution and by-laws on which
much work had been done by the Executive Committee, and electing
the new Executive Committee. One important topic of discussion
was the structure of NCFI. Although the General Committee – who
became the Council of National Representatives (CNR) under the
new constitution – was the policy-making body (with the Executive
Committee executing these policies) it was difficult to fulfil this
function due to lack of continuity and stability, since it met only once
every four years, and often delegates were new to it. For example, only
a third present in 1984 had attended previous meetings, even though
countries were asked to choose as one of their representatives someone
who had. So the Executive Committee were asked to investigate the
structure of other international organisations and possible alternative
structures for NCFI.

The twelve members of the new Executive which met for the two
following days were from seven countries spread over five regions–
Africa, CANA (USA, but one had worked for twelve years in Ecuador),
Europe, CAME (Dora Abraham was the first Indian member on the
committee), and PACEA – but were still elected as individuals rather
than regional representatives. Evangeline Creighton, from Scotland,
became the new Vice-President, but Grace Wallace continued to
contribute her valuable experience from her fourteen years on the
committee – four of which were as President and four as Vice-President.
The committee members faced a long agenda with the various matters
passed to it by the General Committee, including setting up a working
group to investigate alternative structures for NCFI, and making plans
to implement other decisions.

Other related issues discussed were priorities for NCFI work according to its aims and needs expressed by the General Committee, staff roles, commitment to improve communication of NCFI activities and to encourage regional development, and of course the necessary financial resources and budgeting for NCFI work. There was thanksgiving that the cost of the conference and sponsorship for participants who needed it was met, with sources such as the conference offerings and gift stall proceeds completing the amount needed.

As usual members of both committees were working hard, many of them in a second (or third or more) language, after a conference in which many of them had taken a very active part, necessarily supported by God and the prayers of many people around the world. This conference had been a particularly demanding (as well as rewarding) time, and it was a blessing to those involved that afterwards, when safety permitted, they were able to enjoy an outing together into Delhi, and to the grounds of Teen Murti Bhayan also known as Nehru Memorial Museum, where the urn containing Prime Minister Gandhi's ashes was on a small pedestal shaded by a tree and guarded by two Indian soldiers. Committee members were able to file round with many others to pay their respects, and then visit the 'burning ghats'.

There were lighter moments too, such as when a British missionary nurse, twenty-five years in India, used her bargaining skills to help visitors with their shopping, or when the Executive Committee, when the meetings were done, visited the city of Agra and the Taj Mahal, beautiful symbol of India and of love. An unforgettable memory to end an unforgettable conference.

REGIONAL DEVELOPMENT

At the 1976 NCFI Conference, as the benefits and experiences of PACEA (the pilot NCFI Region) were shared and discussed, it was decided to proceed with development of other Regions. The situations, pace of development and the challenges faced were in some ways different in each region, though in other ways similar in several regions. But by the 1980 and 1984 conferences it was evident that development was continuing, and gradually the six Regions came into being. They are considered at this point as, at least in some parts of the world, the regions became increasingly important in NCFI work, and formal regional representation was to become an essential aspect of NCFI structure and governance.

The African Region

Following the 1976 NCFI Conference in Ghana, the delegates of Ghana, Liberia, Zambia and Nigeria discussed their desire to form a Region, and the first Delegates Meeting was held in Nigeria, April 1977. Ezekiel Bagu, President of FCN and holding a senior position in the health service, was asked to act as co-ordinator. When, during a meeting held in Nigeria in 1979 it was decided to proceed with the formation of a Region, he was appointed by the NCFI Executive Committee to be Co-ordinator for Africa for two years, subject to review, but was not a member of NCFI staff.

Only Ghana and Nigeria were represented (by sixteen people from each) at the 1979 meeting, though delegates had been expected from Liberia and Sierra Leone, and Zambia had sent an apology. However, as discussions with the other countries had previously reached an advanced stage with agreement on regionalisation, and those delegates present voted overwhelmingly for it (30 voted 'yes'), a decision was made to proceed with it.

After discussion and with advice from NCFI General Director, Ruth Lichtenberger, who was present for the conference, it was agreed that NCF staff workers of Ghana, Nigeria and Zambia would form the Regional Committee with the Regional Co-ordinator as Chairman. Liberia and Sierra Leone were not represented at the meeting, but had no staff workers as yet. The committee members were, therefore, Ezekiel Bagu (Nigeria) as Chairman, Mary Kusi (later married name Aboagye, Ghana) as Secretary, Liz Wyatt (English staff worker in Zambia), and Micah Tswabki (Nigeria).

At their first Regional Executive Committee Meeting two days later they were joined by Comfort Acheampong, an NCFI Executive

Committee member, and by Ruth Lichtenberger. The new committee discussed relevant parts of the constitution and ways of managing regional finances; and how to pursue their desire to reach out to help other African countries. It was planned that Mary Kusi would visit Liberia to spread the leadership courses she had been teaching in Ghana; that Zambia NNCF would be asked to follow up on the General Director's visit to Tanzania, where there was no NNCF; and to aim to get people from as many African countries as possible to attend the 1980 NCFI Conference, and hold committee meetings there to plan specifically for an African Regional Conference in 1982, in Liberia if possible in order to support the NCF there.

At the 1980 Conference in Denmark there were 12 nurses from 6 African countries, and in 1982 a successful Regional Conference was held in Zambia, as it had not proved possible to hold it in Liberia. There were about 80 full-time participants, with 5 from Tanzania, 6 from Nigeria, 2 from Ghana and a Zambian nurse who was working in Somalia; and in the evenings the numbers were around 150, with nurses bussed in from the local hospitals. The Chief Nurse of Zambia, Mrs Matenda, spoke at the opening meeting, giving a challenge to practise nursing according to Christian principles. This was followed later by Mary (Kusi) Aboagye reporting on her visits to Liberia and Sierra Leone, and presenting a powerful challenge to those present to reach other African nurses. She had visited both countries in 1980 over a period of about three weeks, and her teaching sessions on spiritual and professional aspects were well attended and well received by senior and junior staff in Liberia, despite the tensions after a recent military coup. Potential leaders were identified and included in leadership training.

In Sierra Leone progress was more difficult, not least due to an active HCF and a lack of mature Christian NCF leaders. But at a constructive meeting with HCF it was agreed that the two organisations should have good relationships with each other, and that NCF members could attend HCF meetings, but not hold official positions in HCF, and vice versa. A similar follow-up visit in 1981 was complicated by a recent state of emergency which limited the work done in Sierra Leone, but revealed progress in Liberia which was assisted by more teaching.

During 1981 and 1982, and in addition to the General Director's visits to several African countries, Jan Engle, Ev Waller and Sue Willan (all expatriate Christian missionary nurses working in Africa) visited Kenya, Botswana and Tanzania at the request of the Regional Committee to make nurses aware of the work of NCFI and its constituent NNCFs. There were some HCF groups meeting in some places in these countries, but often little apparent cohesion as a national organisation with international links. In these and other African countries some nurses showed interest and saw the need for an NCF in their own country, particularly if they had been involved in an NCF while studying in other countries, and if help was offered. After visiting Kenya in 1991, Sue Willan was accepted by a mission to work there, work which included pastoral care with medical workers, and so would allow her to help nurses there.

These efforts to reach nurses in other African countries continued over the years, both through Regional Conferences (planned, but not always possible every four years), through the work of the Regional Co-ordinator and Committee as well as others from NCFI, and supported by the stronger NNCFs in Africa, in particular Nigeria and Ghana.

Ezekiel Bagu had already proved to be a leader in FCN Nigeria, and provided leadership as the Region was formed, but in time his work as Chairman and Co-ordinator became limited by health problems. Earlier plans for someone to learn the work as an understudy to provide continuity had not worked out. But God had provided and prepared a successor. Micah Tswabki had become the first Nigerian Travelling Secretary for FCN in 1977, following Grace Stokes, an English missionary. By 1983 there was comment on his Christian maturity, leadership teaching ability, and from 1990 he served as Chairman of the Regional Committee. In 1993, having completed his various professional commitments, he finally became the first full-time Regional Co-ordinator, 'Father Africa' as he was sometimes called by Africans. He served faithfully in this capacity for twelve years, contributing much not only to Africa, but also to the wider NCFI, most evidently at world conferences.

Work in the large continent of Africa has never been easy. Reports and letters over the years mention the challenges posed by frustration and difficulties in travel (such as finance problems, obtaining visas, difficult flights and rough roads, as well as the long distances involved); communication problems (for example unreliable postal systems, phone connections and, later, electricity for fax or computers); political unrest and violence which may have effects on personnel, their work and their families; low economic status nationally and personally, with sometimes a general (local, regional or national) lack of food, basic resources for nursing and for NCF work (even paper and pens), made worse by salaries sometimes not paid for months; and health challenges, most recently the devastating effects of HIV infections and AIDS. But such circumstances compel Christians to exercise faith and depend on God, and thus grow stronger, and the thanksgiving, praise and joy of African Christian nurses has evidently contributed much both at home and at NCFI gatherings.

The European Region

'Not an Easy Delivery' is the appropriate title of a brief history of the birth of the European Region which was written in 2002 – the time of its twentieth anniversary – by Grete Scharfe, a Danish nurse who had been involved throughout. A European conference (rather than a full NCFI conference which was held in Europe) was held in 1974, but that was arranged by the NCFI Executive Committee. However there was a growing desire amongst some European nurses to have a European forum within NCFI, which was confirmed by decisions at the 1976 NCFI General Committee to encourage regionalisation.

On the plane returning from that meeting, six nurses involved in the NNCFs of Denmark, England, Scotland and Switzerland held an informal meeting and planned that there should be a further meeting in 1977 to proceed further towards forming a European Region, and that the two European NNCFs not represented, Austria and Spain, should be invited.

Starting in 1978, staff workers and key leaders from England, Wales and Northern Ireland (one NNCF, often referred to as England for brevity), Scotland, Switzerland, Germany and Denmark met for two or three days once or twice a year for personal encouragement, support, and prayer for their ministries, attending each other's conferences or meeting at NCFI Headquarters in London. Although the NNCF in England continued to be supportive of and involved in these meetings, had always welcomed participation by others in their conferences, and some individuals were in favour of a Region, many questions were raised by the NCF Council. Starting with a response to a memo from Johan Allan about the meeting on the plane, the Council continued to raise concerns, by letter or in meetings between NNCF England and NCFI leaders. The basis for the many questions initially appeared to be concern that commitments might have been made unjustifiably on behalf of NCF England by individuals at the meeting, and then that the autonomy of individual NNCFs might be undermined (including how they used their resources), and that a formal NCFI Region would be an additional layer in a hierarchy, rather than 'an encircling band'.

Despite repeated reassurance, including reference to NCFI committee minutes and guidelines, NNCF England as a whole remained unconvinced of the need for a formalised Region, and was not ready to join one, though some individuals were.

> That decision was received with deep regret by the other European Fellowships. NCF England, Wales and Northern Ireland was the largest of the European NCFs, it had much to offer, and we wanted so much to have them with us as partners in forming the Region.
> (Grete Scharfe, 'Not an Easy Delivery', 2002)

But delay could not continue indefinitely.

At the 1980 Delegates Meeting, NCF work in European countries was reviewed, outreach planned, and the future purpose and functioning of the Delegates Meetings explored. These discussions resulted in a recommendation that 'National Fellowships in Europe form a region now within the established NCFI guidelines on regionalisation'. After much prayer, consideration and with the help of NCFI Headquarters, guidelines for forming a region were sent to NCFI member NNCFs in Europe for discussion, with an invitation to send delegates to a meeting in Switzerland in 1981 (Scharfe, 2004, 2–3).

In response, two of the functioning NNCFs in Europe (Denmark and Scotland) confirmed agreement with the recommendation and one (England) did not. Individuals from four countries without active or well-developed Fellowships indicated a desire for regional development. From the eleven delegates at the meeting, Trudi Streiff (Switzerland), Evangeline Creighton and Nanette Neil (Scotland), Bjørg Finnbakk (Norway), and Grete Scharfe (Denmark) were asked to be the Caretaker Committee until elections could be held the following year. Their main task was to plan and organise the first 'real' European NCFI Conference in Switzerland in 1982.

Fifty European nurses attended that successful conference with the theme 'Beyond Survival: A search for a positive life-style in professional stress'. Held in a beautiful mountainous area, it was at this conference that the first European Regional Committee was elected. This consisted of the people on the Caretaker Committee with the addition of Helga Seemann (Germany), Karen Margarethe Gaarn-Larsen (Denmark), and Grace Stokes who was English, but had previously worked for many years in Nigeria, helping to develop the strong NNCF (known as FCN) there.

From that time on European Committee Meetings were held at least annually, with members elected every four years. Europe had no Regional Co-ordinator for twenty-five years or more after becoming an NCFI Region, but was blessed with a series of effective Regional Chairpersons, of which Evangeline Creighton was the first. Each brought different gifts to the work in addition to Christian commitment and maturity, as did other committee members, and some brought experience from very senior professional positions. For example, guidelines defining the structure, membership requirements, purpose and detailed aims of the European Regional Committee and ways of achieving them were written by the Caretaker Committee, together with Ruth Lichtenberger and Barbara Simsen. There were additional notes on functioning of the committee, responsibility, and relationships with other parts of NCFI. Their conclusions included:

We see that the Regional Committee is the servant of and responsible to the countries forming the Region. At the same time it is also responsible, as an NCFI committee, to the General

Committee through the Executive Committee and General Director ... The Regional Committee, then, endeavours to interpret and fulfil the goals and policies of the General Committee in the light of the expressed needs of the region; the expressed wishes of the countries from that region; the resources available to them. (B. Simsen, committee paper N6-BS-4)

The European Guidelines were given to the elected Regional Committee (for refinement as necessary), the NCFI Executive Committee, and also made available to other regions. With a few small modifications from the PACEA Region, which adopted them in 1982, they considerably developed the Regional Guidelines written earlier by the Executive Committee. At the 1994 European Conference Barbara Parfitt (an experienced English nurse working in a senior university post and also very involved in NCFI) presented a paper on developing a strategy, and it was decided to develop a four-year plan for the Region, leading to budgeting as well as careful financial management.

Developments in committee work, the introduction of the Regional newsletter called *EURONews*, the Regional Conferences held every four years, and other aspects of the work reflect the Regional Committee's use of their gifts and those of other nurses in the Region. As they tried to assist countries where the NCF was 'struggling', and reach out to those where there was no NCF, there was occasional help from Eunice Siccardi, an NCFI staff worker based in Argentina, who agreed to assist in Spain.

The titles of the Regional Conferences, and of sessions within them, reflect the strong professional, as well as Christian, content, and at the 2002 Conference in Norway there were three tracks: leadership, academic and a Health 21 track (related to the World Health Organisation (WHO) goals for Europe and discussed from a Christian perspective). After 1989, when the political 'Iron Curtain' between East and West Europe was removed, the number of countries within the WHO (and therefore NCFI) Region of Europe increased (as some divided) from just over 30 to just over 50. From 1990 there was always participation by at least 3 Eastern European countries in each NCFI European Conference, and from 1990 to 2006 representatives from 16 Eastern European countries attended in total, and in some cases presented sessions. The conferences, Mission '83, Mission '87 (conferences which were open to all, with speakers who were involved in Christian mission) and subsequent general missionary events resulted in many new contacts and opportunities to inform others about NCFI, and its aims, work and resources; and so the work grew.

One challenge was a changing environment over the years, with general decrease in church membership in many of the European countries where it had traditionally been strong, an influx of more people of other religions in some, and the growth of interest in 'New Age' teachings and practices, or in cults. These and other social and professional changes have modified the needs faced in NCF work. Other challenges faced in Europe are in some ways different from those in other NCFI Regions. For many years the 'Iron Curtain' had divided Europe and severely limited contact between nurses in certain areas, and made contact with those outside those areas almost impossible. Behind the Iron Curtain people lived in societies with varying degrees of oppression in daily life, which promoted a lack of trust and communication between people generally, though strong Christians developed even under these circumstances. Then from around 1989 'the walls came down' in the various countries, and freedom increased, though was limited sometimes by cost or visa restrictions.

In 1993, in an attempt to address some of the issues, 22 nurses from 13 countries, 6 of them Eastern European, held a 'Meeting of Friendship and Understanding' for three days in Prague, Czech Republic. The sharing of information about nursing in the different countries, and Bible study together on 'self-worth', 'identity' and 'hope', provided better understanding of the challenges faced, more courage to face them, and a sense of inclusion which was especially important to nurses who had been isolated 'behind the Iron Curtain' for so long. Limitations on freedom to meet, to worship and have fellowship together during former years were vividly illustrated at the 1994 European Conference in Finland, in a very moving mime performed by the Estonian nurses, as one told the history of the development of their NCF, beginning with a group who started meeting in a house for prayer in 1967.

From 1989 there was no longer isolation of Eastern from Western Europeans. But there was some feeling of separation because of the different circumstances, the visible and invisible legacy of so many years of oppression and isolation from much of the world. Many of these countries had missed out on 30 or 40 years of modern development in society and in nursing, and their new 'freedom' was complicated by many problems. NCFI European Region moved from having few contacts in Eastern Europe, with difficulty, to being faced with huge opportunities and needs in many countries, but very limited readily available financial and human resources to meet them. The nurses from Eastern Europe who have attended world NCFI Conferences and/or the European Regional Conferences, have gained from them professionally as well as spiritually, in addition to teaching Western nurses about living their faith in a very different context.

Towards the end of the 1998 Regional Conference in Germany the participants met in country groups to consider what they would take home from the conference and how they could share it with their colleagues. But, as in other parts of the world, it was not easy to go home and start an NCF in their own countries, particularly when their home country was one where many nurses leave home to work abroad for a more adequate salary and conditions, and more opportunities. However there was progress and it was hoped to have the 2010 Regional Conference in the beautiful country of Romania; a plan which would both challenge and support Christian nurses there.

The Latin American Region

In many parts of the world missionary nurses had an important part in the beginnings of NCF work; and it was in Latin America that NCFI staff workers were most involved. At the 1988 NCFI Executive Committee Meeting the staff in Latin America proposed that it should be a separate region, rather than being part of The Americas, because of the great cultural differences between it and North America. But as Latin America had really developed regional work earlier than that, its separate development from earlier times is described here.

In 1969 Lois Cumming, an English missionary nurse who had been working in Argentina since 1961, wrote to Johan Allan expressing her interest in developing NCF work amongst nurses there, beginning with the few being educated in universities. Her mission supported this vision, and at the beginning of 1970 she became the first NCFI staff worker with her mission supporting her financially, and NCFI, in a step of faith, providing £50 per month for her travel and accommodation.

God had prepared her for this work. She was not only a qualified nurse who had taught nurses in Argentina, but she also had a university degree (not in nursing), which was relatively unusual for nurses then. So after attending the professional Argentinian National Nursing Congresses, and addressing them, she had been asked to speak at three of the university schools of nursing. Since in Latin America there were generally relatively few nurses, who had mostly trained at diploma level in hospitals, many of them were anxious and insecure because of the new inexperienced young nurse graduates from the universities who were being put in senior nursing posts, and there were many 'nursing auxiliaries' who might or might not have much training. Lois Cumming made and kept contacts through travel and correspondence and found that there were great spiritual opportunities but little Christian witness amongst nurses. Gradually a few small groups were formed.

In 1974 Fiona Ross, another English nurse missionary in Argentina, felt called to work with nurses. In 1976 she became NCFI staff worker there; and Gaye Mercier, then an Australian nurse missionary in Peru for over ten years, became NCFI staff worker in Peru. Although based in one country and developing the work there they, and others who also worked in Latin America, recognised their commitment to the region and to support each other in the work. The first Latin American NCFI staff workers Conference took place in Lima, Peru in 1977, when Fiona and Gaye met with Nancy Larson (an American missionary nurse who was teaching and working in Ecuador), Marilyn Stewart (an American missionary nurse and advisor in Mexico), and Ruth Lichtenberger (NCFI General Director). Although there were cultural and other differences, many of the challenges faced in the various Latin

American countries were similar – including nurses overloaded with work, with too many patients, few staff and many home responsibilities (most nurses were and are women); the low status of nursing; need for translation of Christian materials for nurses into Spanish or Portuguese; and for time and money to travel and teach.

The staff workers were pioneering, making and following up contacts and explaining what NCF could offer nurses, and nurturing nurses through Bible studies with application to nursing, prayer, and support and fellowship. They were also beginning to do workshops on Christian nurses' role with people who are suffering, and working with Persons in Crisis, ethics in nursing and other such topics, which became welcomed by a number of nursing schools, and reached many nurses and student nurses over the years. Soon after Gaye Mercier had started working with nurses in Peru she asked them what needs NCF could meet which were not already being addressed by churches. The response was that there was no teaching in nurse education about giving spiritual care, and that churches did not understand and therefore could not help them with issues they met in nursing related to ethics, pain, suffering and death. In Latin American countries, as elsewhere, nurses needed help in coping with these issues and helping patients. In the difficult circumstances, teaching nurses and students how to care for themselves and each other was also important.

The same staff workers met for the second time early in 1978, except for Nancy Larson who was only able to send a tape of her recorded thoughts on issues for discussion, known or suggested. No doubt the staff workers prayed for Latin American nurses whom they were seeking to develop, that they would take on the work as leaders. God was about to answer that prayer in an unexpected way.

It was a great shock, not only to her family but also to many of the NCFI family around the world, when in 1978 Fiona Ross was severely injured in a road accident while at Buenos Aires Airport to meet an arriving missionary and died within a few hours. She was remembered by many who had met her at the 1976 NCFI Conference, as well as those in Latin America, as a happy, active person with a deep love of

God, who was building in Argentina on what Lois Cumming had begun. As Ruth Lichtenberger wrote,

> So much prayer is given towards asking for workers in various parts of the world, and this past year we have rejoiced in those whom God called ... How is it possible that, in the midst of these answers to prayer, God chose to remove a worker from an infant movement ? ... Was this a mistake ? ... What about those who were just beginning to understand the vision ? ... God's ways are always perfect.
> (Lichtenberger, 1978, 3)

A successor had already been prepared and introduced to NCFI, though at that time her future importance was not fully recognised. In the first article in the July 1974 edition of *Highway*, Lois Cumming had written about Eunice Siccardi, a mature Christian nurse who had trained in a British hospital in Buenos Aires, worked with three different Christian denominations in Argentina, and then been asked by the province government to organise nursing in the province of Formosa in the north of Argentina. She had recognised her need for more education, and while studying at the University School of Nursing in Córdoba, she saw the need for a Christian voice in the universities, while providing one herself during her studies. Back in Formosa she continued to work with Lois, and later with Fiona Ross.

With Fiona gone there were a few nurses who wanted to help continue the work, but it was Eunice who realised that God, who had called her into nursing, was calling her to become a Christian staff worker amongst nurses, and that she could not do it from where she was. So by 1979 she had left her senior position, moved to Buenos Aires in a step of faith, and was then appointed as an NCFI staff worker, the first who did not have English as a first language. It was soon evident that Argentina had the right staff worker. But Eunice's full contribution to God's work amongst nurses through NCFI became even more visible over many years as she served as an NCFI staff worker in Latin America, at NCFI Conferences and at ICN Congresses, and during visits to Spain to help nurses there to develop a national NCF.

From the first meeting of the Provisional Committee of UCEA (the embryo Argentinian NNCF) she involved other nurses in communicating with other Latin American countries. Even since her 'retirement' in 2000, and despite some health problems over the years, she has continued to serve through NCFI not only in Latin America, but also as an International Board Member.

There were many obstacles to be overcome to hold the first Latin American NCFI Conference in Lima, Peru, in 1982.

> Many delegates had dramatic tales to tell of how they just made it or how God had moved mountains to enable them to come. Then we had a crisis when the bridge between Arequipa and Lima fell down because of an overloaded truck ... Finally we were twenty-seven nurses and students from Argentina, Bolivia, Brazil, Chile, Ecuador, Peru, and the USA who spent the next week building firm friendships, discovering new things about ourselves and about God or relearning things long forgotten and unused, and sharing what God has been doing amongst nurses in South America or what we would like Him to help us to do in the future. It is always thrilling to see God working in people's lives and there was so much evidence of that during the whole week ... But this is just a beginning and I think one of the things we saw most clearly was how much more is still to be done in this vast continent and so few hands to do it. Keep praying.
> (Mercier, 1982, 15)

The work continued and in 1986 the second Latin American NCFI Conference was hosted by the young Argentinian NCF and attended by 60 nurses and students from 7 countries, addressing the theme 'Our commitment as Christian nurses to the society, the profession, and the family'. Gaye Mercier had moved in 1985 from Peru to develop the work in Chile, which she had visited a number of times over the years. It had been difficult to leave Peru after about twenty years (nine years with NCFI), but the rightness of the decision was confirmed as she rejoiced to see the capability of seven Peruvian nurses leading a workshop, and the development of their gifts and confidence. Again this was a time of joy and sharing, but also recognition of the challenges for Christian nurses.

After the conference, and again in 1988, Gaye Mercier, Eunice Siccardi, Nancy Larson and Margaret Corin (who became an NCFI staff worker primarily in Ecuador in 1987) met to discuss the work in Latin America, and their plans, hopes and dreams. Gaye continued with responsibility for Chile, Peru and Bolivia, Eunice for Argentina, Paraguay, Uraguay and Brazil, while Margaret Corin took on the northern Latin American countries. There were still few expatriates and local people committed to developing Christian nurses and nursing in that vast area, but the work of teaching, nurturing and outreach visiting continued and at the third Regional Conference in Ecuador in 1990 there were 105 participants in attendance, representing 11 nations.

The first Regional Committee was formed at the 1990 conference with Alicia Yanez Molina (Chile), Fanny Coto Duran (Peru), Mabel de Martinez (El Salvador), Eunice Gomez de Gonzales (Mexico), Lucy Silva Fernandez (Argentina), Nancy de Mendoza (Ecuador), and Grace de Morillo (Colombia). Grace was to provide important contributions to the region, and to the wider family of NCFI. As a leader, not only amongst Christian nurses in Colombia, but also in the Colombian nurses' professional association, she is widely respected and understands the situation of nurses and nursing not only in Colombia but also in Latin America generally and elsewhere. As the daughter of American missionaries, born and raised in Colombia (though with some education in the USA), and with a Colombian husband and children, she is familiar with both cultures, and speaks English and Spanish with equal fluency. This enables her to communicate the views of Latin American nurses (and contribute to NCFI as an International Board member from 1996) in a way which has been more difficult for others who had the additional effort of mental translation or needed someone to translate for them.

For many reasons it has not proved easy for the committee to meet regularly or to organise the regional conference every four years, and since Gaye Mercier left in 1990, and Margaret Corin left in 1991, only Eunice remained as an NCFI staff worker in Latin America until her retirement in 2000, but the work has continued.

The challenges facing nurses working to develop and spread Christian nurses and nursing in Latin America have included: the position of nurses in society; the low ratio of nurses to patients; low salaries and severe inflation, leading to work overload for nurses doing two or three jobs as well as family responsibilities; inconveniences, problems and sometimes danger from political unrest or military regimes; difficulty and expense of travel over great distances and sometimes mountainous areas; lack of materials for Christian nurses in a language they understand; as well as the challenges faced by Christian nurses everywhere. But when nurses came together through NCFI, as Eunice Siccardi – who by then was functioning as Latin America Regional Co-ordinator – said of the fourth Regional conference, 'Country border, denominations, cultural barriers – all disappeared. The Lord was nearer everyday, healing and refreshing distressed and tired nurses.' (Siccardi, 1994, 2)

Pacific and East Asia (PACEA) continued

This part of the world began to develop as an NCFI Region when, in 1968, the NCFI Executive Committee agreed to Blanche Lindsay's suggestion that it should do so – it was a pilot scheme from which NCFI could learn, as described earlier.

Blanche was NCFI Vice-President from its early days, so understood the work well and, as Federal Secretary for NCF Australia, had already been visiting Asian countries, particularly Singapore, Malaysia and Papua New Guinea under the NCFI 'adoption' (later 'partnership') scheme. She was therefore well prepared to function as a Regional Co-ordinator, and two successful conferences in Singapore (1970) and Penang, Malaysia (1974) helped to strengthen and extend links in the region. NCF New Zealand had been taking a special interest in Fiji and other Pacific Islands and inviting nurses from there to their conferences, and Fiji in turn reached out to other islands. The decision to develop other NCFI Regions was supported by the benefits nurses from PACEA experienced, as expressed at the 1976 NCFI General Committee.

At the third PACEA Regional Conference in 1978, 55 nurses from Fiji, Tonga, Samoa, New Hebrides, Tuvalu, Gilberts, Thailand, Malaysia, Australia and New Zealand, together with 2 from the USA and England, spent 5 days in Fiji living and learning together around the theme 'Walking with the Lord Jesus Christ'. Throughout the conference,

> ... there was a strangely warm feeling of awe, excitement, praise and growing awareness of what it means to have fellowship with one another in a cross-cultural setting. Diversity and difference were obvious in background, life-style, language, custom, food and experience. Yet strong bonds of unity and similarity in Christ were evident in the reality of oneness – something so very hard to express in words.
> (Chappell, 1978, 8–9)

'Faithfulness', 'fun', 'feasting', 'fruit', 'flowers' and 'fragrance' were some of the words used to sum up other aspects of the conference, such as the country reports, trips and tours, hospitality and other joys of Fiji. There were many stories too of how nurses had raised money for conference sponsorship – one Fijian NCF group had made and sold lunches to their colleagues for a whole year to raise funds, and a successful choir competition and other activities in the New Hebrides were held to provide for one person's fare and fees. Nurses in Australia and New Zealand continued their generous support.

In 1979 PACEA entered a new stage in its development when Blanche Lindsay resigned from being PACEA Regional Co-ordinator. She had played an important role not only in NCFI as a whole, but also in the conception and birth of the Region and had nurtured its early development, continuing to do so when she moved from NCF Australia staff into rehabilitation and palliative care nursing (*Highway*, No. 70, 1979/1, 6). With increasing professional responsibilities she left PACEA leadership in 1979 and the NCFI Executive Committee in 1980.

The need for leadership training had always been recognised (but still existed), and there were nurse leaders and a Caretaker Committee in the Region. But it was not easy for them to meet. However delegates and other participants from a number of PACEA countries met at the 1980 NCFI Conference, where they not only presented a lively and enjoyable representation of the Region, but also provided new members for the Executive Committee elected there. From 1976 Alison Chappell (New Zealand), Naty Lopez (Philippines) and Nita Nery (Philippines but resident in the USA) had joined Blanche Lindsay on the committee. In 1980 as Blanche left, Chan Kum Sum (Malaysia) came into the committee, another leader in her own country and Region.

Naty Lopez had already been active in the PACEA Region as well as NCF Philippines, and in 1981 was appointed as full-time Regional Co-ordinator. As she began to prepare for the 1982 conference it was not possible for the Caretaker Committee to meet, though she met two of them individually during visits. There were six NCFI member countries in PACEA – Fiji, Malaysia, Singapore, New Zealand, Australia and Philippines – but only the last two had NCF staff workers. She was already doing leadership and spiritual care workshops, and in 1982 there was a five-day Leadership Training Conference in the Philippines, before the main nine-day Regional Conference.

Twenty-two NCF leaders from New Zealand, Australia, Singapore, Malaysia and the Philippines enjoyed Bible Studies on 'The Personal Life of a Leader', and other aspects of leadership in NCF work, and most recommended that similar sessions should precede the next conference, perhaps also including time management and small group strategy. Two participants expressed their desire to become full-time staff, and it was hoped that others might do so later.

Ninety-four participants from eleven countries were at the main conference (twelve counting Thailand where a missionary nurse was working), and the opening ceremony was attended by leaders from the Council of Deans and Principals, Philippine Nurses Association Board of Governors, and Association of Nursing Service Administrators. The lone delegate from Taiwan, Mrs Katherine Han, had recently been approached to start an NCF there, and was much encouraged by what she saw and heard, taking NCF materials home with her. Comments from some of the participants showed how the aims of the conference were fulfilled – for example 'I want to be salt and light in the world, starting with my own place of work.' 'I have seen how the Lord can use

NCFI Conference 1958, Moscia, Switzerland, where the NCFI Constitution was ratified by the General Committee and the Fellowship was officially born

NCFI Conference 1964, Alpbach, Austria

NCFI Conference 1976, Legon, University of Ghana – the first main NCFI Conference held outside Europe

NCFI Conference 1996, Hong Kong

Executive Committee 1964: (L–R) Betty Kettle, Agathe Burki,
Miss C Spies, Francis Grim, Johan Allan, Miss E.J. Wyatt, Margaret Smith,
Anna Svea Andersson, Blanche Lindsay

Executive Committee 1980: (Front row, L–R) Comfort Acheampong, Evangeline
Creighton, Grete Scharfe, Josefina (Nita) Nery, Chan Kum Sum, Grace Wallace.
(Back row, L–R) Betty Kettle, Pat Ashworth, Dimity Compston, Ezekiel Bagu

NCFI General Committee members, Kolding, Denmark, 1980

Executive Committee and NCFI staff meeting *c.*1989: (Front row, L–R) Barbara Simsen (staff), Eunice Siccardi (staff), Micah Tswabki; (Back rows) Dimity Compston, Bjorg Finnbakk, Mary Aboagye, Dora Abraham, Margaret Corin (staff), Gaye Mercier (staff), Mary Thompson, Helga Seeman, Evangeline Creighton, Erna Goulding, Beverley Chappell, Ruth Lichtenberger (General Director)

First International Board, 1996: (Back row, L–R) Hanna-Leena Nuutinen, Lili Makutu, Erna Goulding, Sita di Monti, Catherine Robertson, Micah Tswabki (staff), Ruth Lichtenberger (retired General Director), Harry Louden (new General Director), Mary Thompson (new President), Eno Egbe, Pat Ashworth, Grace Morillo, Margaret Street; (Front row, L–R) Chieko Fukushima, Esther Sirra, Mary Aboagye, Bishnu Rai, Barkat Dass, Anne Workman, Elizabeth Kalunga, Eunice Siccardi (staff)

NCFI stand at the 1997 International Council of Nurses Conference – Harry Louden (General Director) and NCFI veteran Grace Wallace wait for the rush between sessions of nurses wanting literature, information and contact

NCFI Conference literature, with themes centred around Christian faith
and the profession and practice of nursing

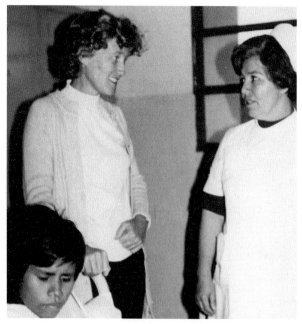

Lois Cumming (back left), a UK missionary nurse and the first NCFI
staff field worker, shown with a nurse and patient in Argentina

NCF and NCF grads in their place of work and in the nursing profession.' 'Relationships developed in small groups ... plan to continue through correspondence and sharing materials etc.' 'Country reports – more specific prayer. Can now give a wider vision to nurses in our own country.' (*Highway* No. 85, 1983/1, 12–13, 17)

At the Delegates Meeting the 13 delegates from 6 NCFI member countries reviewed the Region – Hong Kong and Korea with NCFs but not yet NCFI member countries; Japan with Chieko Fukushima (a Japanese nurse who had encountered NCF during study in the USA) wanting to do NCF work, and three seconded missionary nurses making some progress in the north; Tonga with an NCF group meeting; and Taiwan with plans to start an NCF; and missionary or other contact in other countries. In Thailand there was HCF work and it had been recommended that there should be no more NCFI exploration for two to three years. The Regional Co-ordinator also gave her role description and asked for delegates' expectations of her, which led to useful discussion, and identification of activities under the headings Co-ordinating, Organisational, Regional Activities (committee and conference), Leadership Training, and Pioneering. She would also produce a Newsletter quarterly.

It was proposed and unanimously voted by the delegates that the Co-ordinator should convene the Regional Committee, with power to appoint officers as required, and it was decided to support Japan (through Chieko) as the outreach country. The Regional Committee, chaired by the Co-ordinator, comprised Chan Kum Sum – known often in NCFI as Kum Sum, her family name being Chan – (Malaysia), Peniana Cokanasiga (Fiji), Felicidad Elgado (Philippines), Margaret Hutchison (Australia), Alison Chappell (New Zealand), and Ng Kim Choo – often known as Kim Choo – (Singapore), and met after the conference with Nita Nery (NCFI Executive Committee) also present. Their considerations included more about leadership training, and revision of the guidelines proposed by the European Region (1981). They also decided that of the surplus money from the conference 40 per cent should stay for the region, 30 per cent go for the next NCFI Conference in 1984, and 30 per cent go to NCFI designated PACEA Outreach, for support for Japan. From late 1981 to early 1986 Naty

Lopez remained a very active Regional Co-ordinator for PACEA.

Around 110 delegates from 15 countries attended the fifth PACEA Conference in Singapore in 1986. Almost all the countries in the region were represented, including Indonesia for the first time. The theme was 'Nursing with a difference' and participants gained a wider insight into NCFs around the world, and the need for their ministry.

> We saw that Christians can be change agents, that God's mission for Christian nurses includes responding to social problems. The vision of many was widened as they were led to look to themselves, then to fellow nurses, and on to the nursing profession and to the world in general.
>
> (*Highway* Vol. 2, 1986/3, 11)

Some had their first experience of leading a group, praying aloud, and gaining confidence using their English. A partnership scheme was arranged with the seven member countries each 'adopting' a developing NCF. By this time seven of the NNCFs in the Region had staff workers (with Chieko Fukushima starting part-time staff work in Japan in July) and all the others were asking for one. A week of staff training was planned, and held very successfully, in Singapore in 1997. Eleven nurses from 6 countries each presented 2 topics in talks or workshops, and were evaluated at the end, with Ruth Lichtenberger, and Barbara Simsen (NCFI staff) present as resource persons. Evaluations were given with love and honesty in a supportive atmosphere, and comments from participants reveal some of the impact on them,

> Despite cultural differences God's reconciling love knitted us together as one body ... I was affirmed in the gifts God has given me and became aware of areas I need to work on in myself.
>
> (*CNI*, No. 4, 1987, 6–7)

Challenges faced in the PACEA Region include great cultural and lifestyle differences between member countries, and considerable economic and political changes and challenges in some places. The great geographical distances between countries and the time and cost involved in travel make it difficult for the Regional Committee to meet at times, and there has not been a Regional staff worker for many years. Yet the work has continued to grow, and NNCFs continue to reach out to help others, and to use opportunities when nurses from one country spend time in another for education or work to make contacts, to support and help to develop their knowledge and love of God, and to help them to apply their faith in practice.

Central Asia and the Middle East (CAME)

India, with its huge area and many states and languages which make it in some ways almost like a region, had been involved in NCFI from the 1960s. There had been contacts with groups of Christian nurses meeting in Pakistan and Bangladesh, and many nurses from these countries went to work in the Middle East, which was therefore included in the proposed region. But by 1992 it had not been possible for a functional region to be formed, not least because of the political as well as financial and other barriers to travel. So some delegates had attended conferences in the PACEA Region.

However a new and enthusiastic NCF in Nepal had been formed, and when ENFI (the Indian NNCF) held its third Triennial Conference in 1993, there were delegates from Pakistan and Nepal present. However Pakistan NCF had problems and later ceased to be a member of NCFI, though there have continued to be some contacts with people there. Nurses in Sri Lanka have showed interest at times, but no strong fellowship developed there. NCF Bangladesh has developed and became a member of NCFI in 2005. Throughout the years the NNCF in India has continued, despite political and religious as well as economic and other challenges, with faithful staff workers such as Jessie Allen and Lily Bonner, and other nurses who have contributed to leadership within NCFI as well as the NNCF, such as Dora Abraham and Esther Sirra and others.

ENFI have continued to invite other NNCFs to send delegates to their conferences, and some visits have been possible to other countries within the region. The re-structuring of NCFI from 1996 would provide for the first time a means of more regular meetings between leaders from more than one country in the region and the opportunity for some 'regional thinking' together. But the barriers mentioned previously, and others such as repeated major floods, continue to challenge leaders to find ways of functioning more fully as a region.

Caribbean and North America (CANA)

Since the NNCF of the United States of America joined NCFI in 1970 it had not only contributed leaders (Grace Wallace was the second President), and regular financial and other support, but had also had a very international role within the country because of the number of overseas nurses who came from many parts of the world to study and work there. Some of these nurses, such as Chieko Fukushima from Japan, not only learned much about NCF there, but continued to receive support of various kinds after leaving to build up NNCFs in their own countries.

When Canada became an NCFI member country in 1990, with Anne Workman as staff worker, it was possible to begin to form the Region. Members of the two NNCFs attended each others' conferences, and by 1992 their leaders had held two meetings and were trying to make contact with other countries in the region. These efforts have continued, and there have been some contacts with nurses in countries such as Haiti and Jamaica, but so far none of these other countries have developed strong NNCFs.

It is evident from the above accounts that, by the late 1980s to early 1990s, several of the NCFI Regions were beginning to develop their identity and function, and innovations such as fax and email would contribute a great deal to improving the necessary communications – though in some places the necessary electricity and functioning telephone lines may not always be available, and of course the human element of actually communicating remains! NCFI was moving into a time of changes in location and structure, but not in its purpose of doing God's work amongst nurses worldwide.

THE ONGOING WORK OF NCFI AS A WHOLE

Since 1976 there had been considerable developments in NCFI as a whole organisation. For a time there were six NCFI staff, with Ruth Lichtenberger as General Director, Barbara Simsen as Associate Director for Professional Concerns, Gaye Mercier, Eunice Siccardi and Margaret Corin in Latin America, and Naty Lopez in PACEA. Apart from working locally, all travelled outside the countries in which they were based, to provide teaching, support and encouragement to nurses in NNCFs or in countries which had none.

For them, and for staff who served at other times, life was often not easy. It was difficult sometimes to see so many opportunities and so much work which appeared necessary, when funds were not available to do it. Travel brought rewards of helping in God's work amongst nurses, new contacts and friends, teaching, and seeing people develop. But it was often demanding, and might mean difficult and perhaps dangerous journeys, being on the move and meeting new groups almost continually for several weeks, with little time to relax or do normal daily activities.

When there was opportunity these staff also contributed to conferences, and to discussion and development of NCFI as a whole. There were sometimes questions as to why NCFI had three staff in Latin America, and not elsewhere. But God was working in the churches there, and also called nurses whose mission societies allowed them to serve with NCFI there. Staff members needed their own local support systems, but also support from NCFI, and not just from the General Director. From their reports and discussion at Executive Committee, General Committee and individually, people learned of some of the challenges and difficulties faced as well as the rewards of what was being achieved, and recognised the need to provide support and prayer for the staff as people, not just as staff members. A letter or postcard could mean a lot to someone working in a relatively isolated situation – isolation that can occur even when there are many people around. Committee minutes record the Executive's thanks to staff working 'where terrorism and political unrest are a way of life'. Such conditions are, of course, also faced by nurses in their own countries and NNCFs at times.

In 1979 Betty Kettle resigned from editing *Highway*, NCFI's magazine, which had always been a vital communication and information link with members and others who might be interested in NCFI's work. She had been the editor for nine years, had developed the journal further and made every effort to increase the number of subscribers. It had never been (and was possibly never to be) self-supporting because of the number of copies going to countries where nurses could not afford the cost. But in 1987, with Barbara Simsen as Editor, the name changed to *Christian Nurse International* (*CNI*), and with increasing professional content, the journal was listed in the International Nursing Index and in CINAHL, along with other professional nursing journals. This meant that nurses searching for articles on particular topics would find any relevant articles in *CNI* even if they had known nothing of NCFI, and might gain interest in it in addition to using a particular article.

The Executive Committee at its annual meetings, in addition to the usual work of NCFI, had been working with staff on policy documents and constitutional and by-law changes as these became necessary, in accord with decisions made at the quadrennial General Committee meetings, eventually producing a manual. Such things may seem bureaucratic, but are necessary to provide continuity and consistency, particularly in an international organisation whose committees meet relatively infrequently. Many nurses do not much like paperwork and administration, but NCFI has always been blessed with some nurse leaders with gifts and experience in this area, such as Erna Goulding (USA).

Other concerns at such meetings were budgets, income and expenditure. It was often a source of frustration, particularly to the staff, that they could not do work which they saw as necessary because money was not available. The General Director and Executive Committee worked long and hard, and prayed much to keep the balance between faith in God and Christian responsibility in financial matters. Again NCFI was blessed with people on the Executive Committee like Grace Wallace and, later, Mary Thompson who had, amongst other gifts, those of financial management and fund-raising, with great experience in these areas as Director of NCF USA.

The difference in practices in many different countries meant that people brought different perspectives and experience to meetings. For example, in a discussion at the General Committee on staff salaries it was evident that while some NNCFs paid their staff a salary which bore some relationship to those in professional work (though at a relatively low level), others paid the bills first and their staff with what was left over, and some staff lived in faith on what was given for them. NCFI had salaries set taking into account the cost of living in the country concerned and nursing salaries, on the Biblical principle that 'the labourer is worthy of his hire', but it is sometimes difficult for staff in the situation and committed to the work. So on discovering that headquarters salaries were sometimes paid late, the President pointed out that if such a problem arose she must be told, as this was an Executive Committee responsibility.

Despite the relatively low salaries of nurses in many places and economic difficulties in various parts of the world, the Lord provided resources and the work continued. But one of the matters of financial concern by 1986 was that the interest-free loan from NCF USA, for the purchase of the property in Penge for NCFI Headquarters, was not being repaid.

5

1988–2004: CHANGES AND MOVING TOWARDS REGIONAL REPRESENTATION

NCFI HEADQUARTERS ON THE MOVE

By 1980 the small office at the Church Missionary Society in central London – shared by the General Director and Secretary – was obviously too small for the growing work of NCFI. A property was found and purchased in the less expensive but easily accessible area of South London, at 42 Station Road, Penge. The price was very reasonable, and the property would provide some living accommodation as well as office space, but considerable work was needed to make it fit for use.

NCF USA had provided a loan, interest free for three years, for the purchase, and a further loan at 8 per cent interest for the repairs. At the 1980 NCFI Conference in Denmark the Nehemiah Project, with the slogan 'Be a brick, buy a brick', was launched for NCFI's new home, and many individuals and countries bought bricks for £10 each.

People also contributed in other ways. The work needed on the property proved to be very extensive, and Ruth Lichtenberger (the General Director), with Barbara Simsen (who had moved to work from London for a time), lived and worked amongst the disorder entailed by renovations for many months. Apart from their usual NCFI work, they also organised and supervised the work done necessarily by contracted workers, and worked themselves on decoration and other aspects, sometimes together with NCFI visitors from other countries.

Men from the local parish church had provided transport for the move to Penge, and soon a group of volunteers from there regularly helped with sending out *Highway*, and providing other support, including prayer for the work of NCFI. Holding the annual Executive Committee there at times helped to reduce the cost of accommodation, and allowed its members to see the work and progress, though even with volunteer help this inevitably made more work for the staff.

After a few years the building had been transformed and was

completely occupied by NCFI. When the contract to rent out some office space ended, NCFI lost the extra income, but gained much-needed space. At last there was more adequate room to work on *Highway* and conference materials, and for the volunteers packaging the journals for dispatch four times a year.

Despite the advantages of the headquarters at Penge, by 1986 it was becoming evident that it was not practical to hold staff training courses there, as some had hoped, and the neighbourhood was changing to become less suitable as a location for NCFI's home. There was concern too that although money had come in to repay the £10,000 loan for repairs fairly quickly, it had not yet been possible to begin to repay the purchase loan as the world economy had changed and income barely covered basic expenditure.

However, the value of the building had increased to four or five times its purchase price, so sale would allow repayment of the loan and a reserve fund, and once again the question of where NCFI should be based began to be considered, recognising that, for such an international organisation, the best location might not be in the UK. Ruth Lichtenberger sums up briefly the relocation, a process involving considerable thought, prayer and work over several years by the staff and Executive Committee and others, and the upheaval in her own life.

Finding the best location for NCFI wasn't easy. The world had been considered, various international organisations were asked for their advice. Finally Warrington (halfway between Manchester and Liverpool) seemed an ideal location from the perspective of national and international travel. God soon provided local people who knew people who knew people to help us with property rental and various other areas of assistance needed.

The CNR in 1988 had resolved that the loan should be repaid, and given the Executive Committee responsibility for any re-location of Headquarters. December 1988 was the time to move, an office was found, a house for the General Director was ready. But the sale of 42 Station Road fell through. The 'die was cast.' The post office box had been changed. Suddenly the new location was Ruth

Lichtenberger's spare room. It felt like we were back in the office at Waterloo. And Station Road didn't sell until 1990. However the agreement for the original offices obtained in Warrington had also fallen through. It was February 1991 before the remains of NCFI's possessions came out of storage into 11 Winmarleigh St, ideally located in the town centre of Warrington.
(Lichtenberger, 1998, 8–9)

CHANGES IN NCFI STAFF

In 1989 Barbara Simsen resigned from being NCFI Associate Director, though she continued to work part-time for NCFI, editing *CNI* until the end of 1991. Originally appointed in 1976 to teach workshops on topics such as spiritual care and 'Persons in Crisis' where NNCFs wanted help in these areas, she had done this and much more. Based in London most of the time while not travelling, she had contributed in many ways, working with the General Director on conferences and other materials, editing NCFI's journal, and deputising for Ruth while she (Ruth) was on study leave doing a diploma in counselling.

The Executive Committee had supported the policy of study leave for long-term staff, in the belief that they must be allowed such opportunities for development and renewal if they were to continue to fulfil their potential to serve in NCFI. Life-long learning was becoming expected of nurses in many countries, and NCFI staff must be fitted to work amongst them.

During her study leave Barbara won a scholarship for the second year of her Master's course in Manchester University, and her research was recognised as making a good contribution to the sparse knowledge and literature on spiritual care in the UK and elsewhere. In her final editorial she said,

It is with a sense of grief that I hand over the reins of the magazine and move to Hong Kong to take up a new appointment. *CNI* will remain close to my heart for many reasons. Whilst it has certainly had its frustrations, it has also been a source of enjoyment and

learning. It has been a means of encouraging myself and others to reflect on what it means to be a Christian and a nurse, and to express that faith in our professional practice ... I might be leaving a job – but not the NCFI International family.
(Simsen, 1991, 3)

That was to prove very true when the 1996 NCFI Conference was held in Hong Kong.

In Latin America too there were changes. Gaye Mercier had been seconded to work with NCFI in Peru in 1976, and had made great contributions over the years until 1990 when she moved to other mission work. She had built up and supported the development of NCF in Peru until its leaders could form a committee able to continue the work. After sharing in the work of visiting other Latin American countries during this time, she had then moved to Chile on request, to help in developing an NNCF there. Like other staff she had taken part in 'bringing the world to NCFI Executive' through her reports, giving a sense of life in Latin America, the problems and opportunities, which was essential for relevant prayer, support and planning. Despite difficulties, dangers and lack of desired resources, she had continued, completed a Masters degree in her own time, and helped two new NNCFs to develop. She had also often served as translator, enabling Spanish-speaking nurses to take part in and enjoy NCF International Quadrennial Conferences, a task often little noticed by others, but demanding and tiring along with other responsibilities.

Margaret Corin, who had been working in Ecuador, was appointed in 1987, and finished her term of service with NCFI in 1991. She had continued to develop NCF work in Ecuador, as well as contributing to the work of the region, and the thinking in NCFI generally.

There had been discussions and proposals during the 1980s for changes in structure with more staff. These included plans for an administrator and more secretarial help, since both Ruth as General Director and Barbara Simsen felt that they were not able to focus on using their gifts. When asked at the 1984 General Committee what they saw as their gifts it was evident that none of the NCFI staff believed they had a gift for administration. But it had never proved possible to offer a salary which would attract a suitable person for the post of administrator, despite the General Committee's resolution supporting such an appointment. God had other plans, and by 1992 there remained only Eunice Siccardi in Argentina (but working also with other Latin American countries in the region) and the General Director.

At NCFI's new home in Warrington Ruth was assisted by the latest of a succession of committed and valuable secretaries, each of whom had contributed their various gifts to the work. There was also yet another team of volunteers to help, and later someone to help part-time with administration, and Stan Morris, a volunteer who helped with the database and financial records for a number of years. However NCFI was to have a new overall structure.

DEVELOPING A STRUCTURE TO FIT THE CURRENT WORK

Much had changed since the first constitution of NCFI in 1958, when there were few member countries, travel and postal services often took much longer, and relatively few nurses knew much about other countries. Television was relatively new then, where it was available at all, and for many nurses low salaries and long working hours in hospitals, where they often had living accommodation too, meant that their known world was relatively small. Few nurses were used to formal committee work even at national level.

All this, together with meetings up to four years apart (after the early years), made it difficult for the General Committee to function effectively as the decision-making body in NCFI. The Executive Committee necessarily did much of the work, but while increasingly it included people from five continents and by 1976 all of these were nurses, they were elected as individuals rather than representatives of a region or country.

Over NCFI's first thirty years the world had become 'a much smaller place'thanks to television, increasing air travel and other developments. Nursing had developed professionally in a number of countries, with more nurses involved in committee decision-making, and travelling to professional conferences, or for holidays. NCFI too was changing in some respects. Staff reports and other papers were being prepared and distributed for reading before committee meetings, so that the time at the meeting could be used for discussion and decision-making, and from 1984 Executive Committee minutes (minus confidential matters) were available to any member country on request. So NNCF leaders could be more familiar and up to date with the ongoing work of NCFI as a whole, allowing for the different speed with which communications could reach their country.

At the 1984 General Committee, while discussing changes in the Constitution and by-laws, concern was expressed that there was not sufficient stability and continuity in the committee for it to function well as the decision-making body for the organisation. Despite previous requests to countries that at least one of their representatives should have been at the committee before, only one third of those present had been. There was also concern about the implications as membership increased, resulting in a larger committee. The Executive Committee was asked to set up a Working Group to 'give serious consideration to looking at the organisational structure of NCFI and report back to next year's Executive Committee Meetings'.

Because of sickness and other problems the Working Group was unable to meet in 1985, but in 1986 developed a paper suggesting three possible options for restructuring, This was presented at the Executive Committee, but no formal proposal recommending a change in structure was prepared for the next Council of National Representatives (CNR, formerly the General Committee) in 1988, though the by-laws were strengthened regarding the election of the Executive, and to try to ensure representatives on CNR were truly able to represent their NNCFs and had experience of it.

Review continued, and the process over several years of consultation, prayer, and constructively critical consideration while devising plans for change, was as important for development in NCFI as the eventual implementation. Twenty-three of the twenty-five member countries were represented at the 1988 CNR, and an extra preparatory session was held before the main CNR meetings. The usual two-day meetings tended to be very full and a challenge for those taking part, particularly if it was their first such meeting, given language and procedure differences in different countries. After preliminary introductions of people by name and country, outline of the committee procedure according to the paper, and a check that everyone had the seventeen reports and other papers for the meetings, delegates met in regional groups. They were asked to identify how they saw NCFI working towards its goals over the next four years, generally and within their region, and what resources they had in the region, saw available elsewhere, or needed to be sought.

India, Africa and PACEA all expressed the need for a visit from NCFI staff, for leadership training, encouragement and communication. PACEA and North America emphasised exchange of resources, both material and people, while Europe saw its needs as material on ethics to combat the decline in moral standards in nursing, and personnel and other resources to reach countries with no NNCF. The General Director presented a paper she had prepared in response to hearing some negative comments about NCFI, and the continued lack of financial resources to respond to the great opportunities. In this she reported that countries rarely responded to information sent, or sent information when requested, or completed the prayer request forms; resources were rarely requested from NCFI or shared with them, and NCFI resources such as Bibles Study guides which had been prepared were rarely ordered, though appreciated when they were seen. Few member countries invited neighbouring countries to their NCF activities. She reflected on NCFI's origins, and whether NCFI was doing God's work in the way He intended, and asked the CNR delegates to consider the paper thoughtfully and prayerfully.

Over the next four years the Executive Committee, now chaired by Evangeline Creighton, the new President, worked at and prayed hard over achieving the right plans for change. (The CNR had set aside a by-law to enable Evangeline to serve a fourth term on Executive, to provide continuity.) In 1989 the staff presented to the Executive

Committee a draft paper on professional and other areas of ministry, which had emerged partly through the financial constraints on staff outreach ministry. The final paper, 'NCFI Ministry Objectives and Strategic Priorities 1990–1995' (4011-MSC.WP) was endorsed by the Executive Committee and offered to member countries. An ad hoc committee was set up to 'study where NCFI is in its organisational development to determine what is the appropriate philosophy of ministry and structure for the future.' But in 1990 they felt unable to proceed without a review from the membership of NCFI's influence and effectiveness.

Responses to the first questionnaire showed that overwhelmingly the NNCFs valued and were concerned to continue NCFI's ministry. Responses to the second questionnaire about its functions emphasised linking between Fellowships and nurses around the world; literature which helped nurses to strengthen their NNCFs; and professional outreach and integration of faith with nursing practice. Nurses in some countries had been encouraged to implement a professional focus in their ministry, using NCFI literature, and also become more involved in their professional organisation and submitting articles to professional journals; and greater outreach within their own countries or to other countries, with vision gained from NCFI conferences, materials and staff visits.

Having consulted the membership on the value and influence of NCFI, the Executive Committee met in January 1991 with a Management Consultant from Marc Europe (a division of World Vision), to consider possible structures for NCFI. In April the ad hoc committee reviewed the responses of the committee members to three models, and found that the third model most favoured was very similar to the third model proposed in the 1986 committee, where it was more fully developed. This was therefore taken as the working model, and extended in the plans proposed to the CNR in 1992.

Great thought was given to the preparation for change, and 'A strategy for change', a working paper for the Standing Committee (4033-MSC.DOC), sets out a brief history of how plans were developed, the proposals for change, and a review of the procedure for change, using a Marc Europe paper on change management.

At the 1992 CNR in Fiji, 27 of the 29 member countries were represented (only Liberia and Pakistan were not) and, of these, 16 NNCFs had been sending an annual report to NCFI Headquarters as resolved in 1988. The Strategy for Change paper, draft constitution and by-laws, proposed staffing structure and draft Regional guidelines had been sent out for consideration by member countries. Ten of the twelve elected Executive Committee members were present and they had met four times during the conference and before the CNR, not least to discuss the proposed changes and how best to help the CNR delegates to understand and address them. Margaret Hutchison (Australia) presented the current structure, proposed changes and reasons for them on behalf of the Executive Committee. The present structure was not as effective as desired because:

- The Executive Committee is not representative of NNCFs or Regions
- CNR meets too infrequently to be an effective policy-making and planning body for NCFI work
- National Representatives do not always have the background experience, continuity of involvement, and wider perspective necessary for decisions which need to be made at CNR (CNR Minutes, 1992, 8)

The policy-making body in the new structure would be an International Board, with three representatives from each NCFI Region, with a Standing Committee which would serve the board by implementing plans and policies, and doing special projects as required. The President would be elected from and by the board members. There would be a Regional Forum for each Region, composed of national representatives, who would meet at the Regional and Quadrennial Conferences, and elect their three Board Members. There would also be an International Forum composed of National Representatives, which would meet every 4 years and would make recommendations to the Board. The benefits of this would be:

- More flexibility for future development of NCFI
- More representation for Member Countries, through their Regional representatives

- More informed decision-makers (who will have both a
  national and regional perspective)
  (CNR Minutes, 1992, 8)

The President emphasised that a Board of around twenty-one members, regardless of how many NNCFs became members, would be of manageable size, yet achieve worldwide representation. After a proposal to accept the new structure, duly seconded, there was discussion including reservations about individual NNCFs no longer having the final say in policy decisions, and the cost of getting Board members to meetings. The proposal was finally accepted with 31 in favour, 4 against and 1 abstention. The meeting went on to pass the new constitution, after discussion, but to leave some modification of the by-laws to the Executive Committee, on the basis of the CNR discussion, as the new International Board would not come into existence until the 1996 NCFI Conference.

The proposed staff structure included the General Director, Associate Directors for Administration and Professional Affairs, and an Associate Director for each Region, and a number of reservations were expressed as to whether this could be supported financially. However with the explanation that this was the ideal, it was recognised that it would only be achieved if finance was available. The General Director, appointed by the Executive Committee (or International Board) could only appoint staff within an agreed budget. Ruth Lichtenberger planned to retire as General Director in 1994, after nineteen years with NCFI, and the President had already contacted NNCFs about seeking a successor. Eunice Siccardi (Argentina) too would be due to retire in 1995, and appreciation and thanks were expressed for all their faithful years of work with NCFI. (Eunice did not actually retire until 2000, and even then continued to play an important part in Christian work amongst nurses.)

The new structure would only begin to come into effect after this CNR, so a new Executive Committee was elected. Before election of the President and Vice-President, Evangeline Creighton, who had served a very significant term as President over the past four years of review and planning, reminded the delegates that nominations could come from NNCFs and the Executive Committee. In light of the changes to the structure 'the next four years are going to be crucial', and with that and appointment of a new General Director by the Executive Committee, there would be much to work through, which would demand a lot from the President. As she had only been off the Executive for four years and had been President before, Pat Ashworth (England) had at first declined when asked to stand for election, believing it to be both a responsibility and an honour which should be shared more widely. However she eventually agreed to be one of the nominees and leave the decision to God and the electorate, and was elected as President, with Erna Goulding (USA) as Vice-President.

The period of intensive review was over, and when the first International Board was elected at the next CNR in Hong Kong, NCFI would have a new structure and a new General Director.

NCFI CONFERENCES IN THE USA AND FIJI, AND ICN IN KOREA AND SPAIN

In 1988, the twelfth NCFI Conference was held on the campus of Eastern College, Philadelphia, the USA. Four hundred and fifty nurses from fifty countries met for the conference, with the theme 'By Whose Standards?', but before the main conference week, twenty-one invited nurse leaders from around the world spent two days considering the current and developing needs of the profession; priorities and strategies for meeting them; and reviewing and planning to share resources. From this Christian Perspectives Consultative Summit (CPCS) recommendations to CNR were made for a prayer focus for Christian ministry in nursing, a database to link Christian nurse leaders, teachers, researchers and so on, a cumulative index of Christian literature and resource material, and exchange opportunities for leaders and students. This led, through CNR, to the 'Think 1st and Pray' request to nurses throughout the world to commit for four years to pray on the first day of each month especially for nursing and Christian ministry to it, alone or with others (in addition to praying at other times of course). A database linking Christian nurse leaders was later compiled at NCFI headquarters, but proved difficult to use. A separate index of Christian literature was never completed, but increasingly nurses learned to find sources elsewhere. Some exchange experiences continued to occur, and sometimes the NCFI network proved useful for students planning an overseas elective period.

During the main conference, in addition to Bible teaching by Eugene Petersen, there were plenary sessions related to professional inheritance, ethical choice, clinical practice, and cultural and leadership issues in nursing by Virginia Ohlson (USA), Beverley Chappell (New Zealand), Susie Kim (Korea), Barbara Parfitt (UK) and Chan Kum Sum (Malaysia). Simultaneous translation was available in several languages, and after each of the professional sessions there was a time for group discussion, to encourage people to think through and discuss the issues rather than just listen and absorb. As always there was a wide variety of workshops available, and this conference for the first time had Market Place, a forum provided for anyone who wished to do so to speak for up to twenty minutes about anything related to Christian nursing, provided that they had registered their name and topic in advance. Listeners gathered to hear, and perhaps discuss, as they wished.

Many participants will remember the wooded campus, the hot and sometimes wet weather, the sound of the cicadas, the outings to New York, Washington or the peaceful Pennsylvania Amish country – and the lovely coffee-time cookies made by our hostesses and their friends! Many people had worked hard for the usual 'craft stall' of items brought from many countries. This is one way in which countries unable to give money, and perhaps needing sponsorship money to attend the conference, can contribute with others, and on this occasion the amount raised for NCFI was around £6,000 (the most ever), thanks in part, to the auction of a beautiful handmade quilt.

But such a conference should never end with just the time there, or even reading the papers later. As Dora Abraham (India) said, 'The application of this conference is our responsibility. We must go and LIVE this conference back at home.' (Editorial, 1988, 3) With the difficult circumstances to which many would return, all would need the support to 'Think 1st and pray'.

*

The thirteenth NCFI conference held in Fiji in 1992 was in some ways very different – in environment, in culture and in content. A young Fijian representative, Silima Waqa, was inspired at the CNR in Philadelphia to offer Fiji as the host country for the 1992 conference, and the offer was accepted subject to a formal letter of invitation from the NNCF – who had not yet been asked! This was, to say the least, somewhat of a surprise to the more senior and experienced nurses on the Fijian NNCF Committee when she returned home to report back! They had an active Fellowship, and the committee members made sure that they visited all the groups and reached out to others – but could they host this global conference in Fiji, a small country made up of many islands? However they had experience and faith, and decided that, if the NCFI Executive Committee still agreed when they visited, the Fijians would take it as the Lord's will that they should host the conference. After years of much prayer and fasting they did host it, and 287 nurses from 44 countries enjoyed a unique experience. For staff workers there were four days of training (from 1–5 July), before the conference which took place from 6–13 July.

The Conference, entitled 'Christian Values in Nursing Action', was held in Suva mainly on the university campus. This was at the opposite end of the main island from Nadi, the main airport. So participants were met by NNCF members and, during the bus journey to Suva, had plenty of time to enjoy the beauties of the green and palmy island, with hills in the background, as well as getting to know each other or catching up on news from 'old' friends.

There is a strong Christian tradition in Fiji, and the well-known warm hospitality of the smiling Fijians continued throughout the conference, including an outing to the beach, a boat ride to islands showing different aspects of 'old Fiji', a Fijian feast, graceful dancing by the ladies who 'looked after us' and others, singing and other cultural delights.

The conference began with a fanfare from the Fijian Military Forces Band, and the arrival of Her Excellency Lady Bale Ganilau, wife of the President of Fiji and herself a nurse. After the roll call of the nations, with participants in national dress presenting their flags as usual, and a welcome by Evangeline Creighton (NCFI President) and Lili Makutu (Fiji NCF President), Lady Bale spoke, including the words, 'If we lose our caring role and if we lose those principles of nursing which enable us, then we fail in the development of our profession.' (*NAPS* 8 (3), 1992, 1)

Apart from the morning Biblical Expositions, the format of this conference was different. According to the brochure:

> Christian nurses want to apply their faith to their nursing practice. Theoretical knowledge of what the Bible says is not enough. Thus we must understand the values we should hold. Then we must put them into practice and influence those around us to do likewise.

> This conference is designed so that nurses will:
> * Think about some of the Bible's teaching on current issues facing nurses and examine the values involved
> * Prepare an action plan and materials to communicate to colleagues what has been learned

There were ten symposia in Track A each with sessions spread over the whole conference, on topics such as 'Caring for the Carers', 'Ethics and Justice in Nursing', 'Concepts and Conceptual Frameworks in Nursing', 'Spiritual Care' and 'Forgotten Peoples'. Each participant had opportunity upon registration to choose just one of these on which they had some knowledge, but would like more depth; and participate in a symposium with perhaps two or three papers on the topic, Bible study, prayer discussion and preparation of materials to be presented. Or people who preferred to do so could choose and explore three topics from Track B in less depth. A total of 48 papers were presented by nurse leaders from 19 countries. In the final conference day plenary sessions, Track A symposia participants presented their topics in a variety of ways.

Micah Tswabki, who was at the conference, had been appointed, with the agreement of the African NNCFs, to become the Regional Co-ordinator for Africa – though he would not take up the appointment until 1993 after completing the term in his current work. The conference provided opportunity for distributing cards to pledge prayer and financial support for him (having first checked that this was culturally acceptable).

As always news of other countries was an important aspect of the conference, and multicultural groups leading and participating in the symposia had opportunity to get to know others with similar interests. In addition, during Window on the World sessions, country representatives shared information on the situation amongst nurses and what God was doing in their countries, and NCFI and each country had a stand, with someone there to provide information at fixed times.

At this conference Canada, Chile, Germany and Japan were welcomed as new NCFI members, and Papua New Guinea, Slovenia and Romania were represented for the first time. It was an opportunity for those from Papua New Guinea to get together for the first time – since travel at home was difficult and sometimes dangerous – to form a constitution for a PNG NCF, assisted by Margaret Street, a New Zealand nurse working in that country. Again Market Place offered the opportunity for any participant to 'get on their soapbox' and talk about any issue related to Christian nursing which they felt needed attention.

As always, nurses went home from the conference with more knowledge of nurses and nursing elsewhere, and therefore able to pray more intelligently for them, and encouraged that others would also be praying for them in their situation, whether it be amongst the dangers of difficult travel or political strife, lack of equipment and resources to meet the health challenges, the lack of trust after many years under an oppressive political regime, or the very different challenges of relatively affluent societies with increasingly secular and 'New Age' influences in nursing.

ICN Congresses had been considered important professional occasions for NCFI since 1965, and Christian nurses were well-represented among the 7–8,000 nurses in Seoul, Korea in 1989, and around 10,000 in Madrid, Spain in 1993.

In Seoul, Dame Nita Barrow, Ambassador of Barbados to the United Nations and a Christian nurse distinguished for many activities, received the top award of ICN, the Christiane Reimann Award. There were up to one hundred nurses at the NCFI Prayer Breakfasts each morning and at the last one they were joined by Mo-Im Kim (Korea), and prayed for her as she prepared to accept her role as the new President of ICN with her inauguration that evening. She had become a Christian two years before, influenced by Christian colleagues and, although a well-respected nurse leader before that, positive changes in her were said to be very evident since then. At her first press conference as ICN President, after listing some Congress highlights, she said 'I myself am a Christian nurse. The Christian activities associated with the programme have been a highlight for me,' and went on to make special mention of the prayer breakfasts. (Editorial, 1989, 3)

Every Congress participant had received a bookmark from NCFI and the Korean NCF, with the well-known Prayer of St Francis on one side and the activities of NCFI at the Congress on the other. More than two hundred people enjoyed the reception, with a challenging message from Norma Bryan (Australia), an interesting interview with Susie Tsang of Hong Kong, and Christian music from a Korean choir. It is perhaps not surprising that Mo-Im Kim chose 'Love' as the watchword for her ICN Presidential term.

The location of the 1993 ICN Congress in Madrid had been changed to a new one, which had very modern conference buildings – but was still being finished as the congress began! This presented challenges for those preparing the NCFI stand in the exhibition, as well as those organising events during the Congress (including ICN staff). What was usually a prayer breakfast met at lunchtime one day, and for forty-five minutes before the 10 a.m. session for the next four days, and there were not so many participants as previously. However there was also at least one prayer meeting, organised by some of the participants, going on in a local hotel.

At the luncheon and Open Meeting 120 nurses heard Virginia Ohlson (USA) speak on a Christian perspective of the Congress theme 'Unity for Quality' – a very appropriate theme for Christian nurses, with Grace de Morillo (Colombia) translating into Spanish.

As always there were nurses who encountered NCFI for the first time at the Congress and saw possibilities for their own countries, and many New Testaments and copies of *CNI* in English or Spanish, were given out. For 3 NCFI staff, 8 Executive Committee members (who would meet in committee after the Congress), and 15 volunteers it was an exciting as well as demanding time.

A NEW GENERAL DIRECTOR, REGIONAL REPRESENTATION AND CONFERENCE IN HONG KONG

From 1988 the Executive Committee worked and prayed intensively to devise a structure for NCFI to fit the aims and objectives, and in accord with its stage of development. With minor modification this structure was agreed by the 1992 CNR in Fiji. So, in addition to their usual work, over the next four years the Executive Committee and staff would have the task of helping to smooth the path of implementation of the changes. But alongside this was an even more urgent task – to find and appoint the person chosen by God to be the next General Director, since Ruth Lichtenberger had announced her intention to retire in 1994.

Before 1992 countries had been asked to suggest people who might be suitable applicants and, as suggestions came in, each person suggested was written to and asked if they were considering applying. The post was also advertised in the Christian press.

The General Director's job description was carefully reviewed with the current Director and in light of NCFI's realistic requirements. In addition to 4 NCFI people (past and current Presidents and Executive Committee members, from 3 continents), 2 experienced people from nondenominational Christian international organisations also took part in the interviews, to provide more independent advice. By the end of 1994 there had been no new appointment, but Ruth ceased to be the General Director, as she was moving into a new phase in her life. She agreed to continue part-time mainly to function as co-ordinator for the 1996 NCFI Conference, and to edit *CNI*. There would continue to be a secretary in the office, and Executive Committee members would take on some duties, each relating to their Region.

Finally a new General Director was appointed in early 1995, and started work on 1 May. Harry Louden (Scotland), is qualified as a general nurse, a psychiatric nurse and as a Health Visitor. (In the UK Health Visitors work in the community, most often with healthy children and their parents.) After some years nursing in Scotland, Bible College, and leprosy training in India, he moved with his wife Ruth (also a nurse) and their three children to Papua New Guinea. Eight years with the Leprosy Mission ended with the training materials written, published and in use, and the role he had developed handed over to a New Guinean, and the Louden family returned to the UK, still with the Leprosy Mission for three to four years. God had prepared Harry in various ways for his new role as General Director of NCFI, and a fuller profile is available in CNI 1995 11(2):15.

For the first time NCFI had a male General Director (men are still in the minority amongst nurses in most countries) with a wife and family, like Micah Tswabki, Regional Co-ordinator in Africa. This reflected the reality that in most countries probably the majority of nurses now have family responsibilities, and was perhaps a timely reminder of the need to recognise the extra pressures this puts on their time and other resources, and the value of their family support.

Throughout the four years since 1992, the Executive Committee and NCFI staff tried to help all concerned with moving into the new structure, including reminders about the Regional and International Forums at the conferences, and the nomination and election of the three representatives from each Region for the International Board. The four-day leadership training before the 1996 Conference was planned so that for two of the sessions there would be three tracks: one for national and international committee members, to ensure familiarity with the changes and identify and address possible problems; one for national staff workers; and one for NCF leaders and potential leaders. For the remaining sessions, participants chose from the options of 'Inductive Bible study', 'Myers-Briggs Personality Inventory', 'Writing for Publication', and 'The Buddy System' developed by NCF New Zealand to help new graduates in nursing. There was also a session on fund-raising – very relevant for all, since in the NNCFs and NCFI it remained frequently a challenge to meet the apparent needs. God provides resources, but nurses have to be willing to give, find and work for them.

The 1996 NCFI Conference, 'Equipped to Care: Making a Difference in Nursing and Society', was held from 1–8 July in Hong Kong (where nurses might face changes and new challenges when Hong Kong reverted from British to Chinese government in 1997). Already nursing was affected by the many nurses who were emigrating – like other people who had the skills and resources to do so. Certainly the conference itself, the first for Harry Louden, provided challenges for the Hong Kong NCF Committee and their helpers, for Ruth Lichtenberger as conference co-ordinator, and Barbara Simsen (no longer on NCFI staff but teaching nursing in Hong Kong). It was good that Barbara had prepared a prayer guide covering the preparations as well as the conference as many challenges presented themselves in the preparation for and duration of this conference – owing to building delays, it was necessary to change the main conference location about two months before participants arrived. Then around 400 participants arrived from 46 countries, instead of the 300 planned for, which was good, but provided problems in accommodating those registering late, on another site and without air-conditioning, and meant work, organisation and discipline from all at meal-times to get everyone fed on time. Registration was also complicated by the difficulty in producing essential lists due to the accident suffered just before the conference by Stan Morris (England), a faithful retired non-nurse friend of NCFI who worked for some years on NCFI accounts and database. (Stan was sad to miss the conference too.)

Despite all this, and the test of some people's patience by consequent delays and inconvenience in registration, it was a great conference and the Hong Kong nurses proved excellent hostesses/hosts, with attention to details. For example, every participant's badge had on the back the address of United World College, the conference site, in Chinese, to show if people got lost while out and needed a taxi driver to get them 'home'.

At the opening ceremony roll call, in the Chapel of the Chinese University, there was a special welcome for Estonia, Papua New Guinea, Nepal and Taiwan, the new member countries of NCFI. After other welcome messages, an address was given by Ms Susie Lum, the Senior Executive Manager (Nursing) for the Hospital Authority of Hong Kong; this was not an easy time for her with so many nurses concerned about the expected changes in 1997 and the possibility of having to move to other countries. Music on a Chinese stringed instrument was beautiful and unusual for many of those present.

The Bible expositions by Revd Wilson Chow on the book of Daniel were followed each day by professional sessions on different aspects of the main theme, presented by Shirley Wong (Hong Kong), Esther Sirra (India), Barbara Parfitt (UK), Grace de Morillo (Colombia) and colleagues, and Susie Kim and Won Hee Lee (Korea), all Christian leaders in education and other aspects of nursing. All provided thought-provoking material, but some of the strongest reactions, positive and negative, resulted from Barbara's paper on 'The Rights of Christian Women in Nursing'. In an organisation composed of nurses from so many different family, cultural, environmental and church backgrounds, inevitably not all agree on everything. For example, from early in NCFI's history it had been a challenge for the organisers to find inclusive ways of conducting the conference Service of Holy Communion, given the many different traditions of participants. But the ability of people to focus on the essentials of Christianity and the profession which we share, and to be challenged to learn from one another despite (or sometimes because of) differences, is one of NCFI's strengths. 'Unity in Diversity' (the title of one of the regional conferences) is one of God's great gifts.

As usual there were in Hong Kong numerous and varied concurrent sessions to choose from and, in line with professional developments generally, requests and guidelines for submission of abstracts had been sent out, and permission for publication was requested. Each Window on the World evening session started with a short devotional time and presentation from a Region, followed by visiting the Region's country displays and presentation of information often outside in the pleasant cooler air of the evening. The forum for each Region met, the International Forum was held for the first time, and the new International Board with three members elected by each Region was introduced.

The craft stall was busy between sessions, and again produced a healthy contribution to NCFI resources of over USD $5,500, as well as interesting souvenirs or presents for people to take home. Two innovations were the beautiful National Dancing Display by nurses from several countries, and the table tennis tournament organised by Barbara Parfitt's young son Simon. However the youngest conference participant was a baby girl brought along by her mother, Tove Giske (a Christian nurse leader in Norway), and her husband. For some participants it was probably educational to see him sharing in childcare while Tove was occupied with conference activities.

Visits to hospitals or other healthcare centres allowed participants to see nursing in an environment perhaps very different from their own, and gain new understanding and ideas, and as always the 'day out' and Cultural Evening were times for enjoyment and fun together. The views over Hong Kong from Victoria Peak were amazing, the food at the 'floating restaurant' was excellent and some visitors acquired new skill with chopsticks. Stanley Market was fascinating, as other people's markets always are; the New Territories and islands were beautiful, and all these were more enjoyable when shared with new friends, or 'old friends' usually separated by many miles. Highlights of the evening, viewed from out on the terraces by the swimming pool, included the traditional Lion Dance, a demonstration of large scale calligraphy of the Chinese character for 'Blessing', a few words from a nurse from China (who could not at that time be included in the participants' contact list), and finally 'The Great Race' which involved various NCF/NCFI leaders first eating a bowl of rice with chopsticks as fast as possible – with the 'locals' using their left hand to even the contest; and in the final heat feeding each other!

Perhaps three of the comments overheard and recorded in *Care Times*, the conference daily news-sheet, sum up how many nurses have felt about this and other NCFI Conferences –

> 'There is so much work to do in my country amongst nurses, and especially Christian nurses. I am gaining so much knowledge here.

Learning about leading inductive Bible studies helped a lot. Also, the professional sessions are high quality.'

'The best part of being here is the joy of being together and seeing so many races.'

'I have no doubt that God is working through nurses called by Him around the world, after hearing the wonderful singing at the Opening Ceremony. That chorus of praise was quite a testimony.'

For some of those present there had been many years when such things could not have happened in their home country.

NCFI AT THE 1997 ICN CONGRESS

The twenty-first ICN Congress, 'Sharing the Health Challenge' was held in 1997 in the beautiful city of Vancouver. Some NCFI people had already just met at the Canadian NCF's first national conference, 'Building Bridges', which had been held nearby, and others would go afterwards to the USA NCF Conference at Cedar Campus, not too far across the border.

The opening ceremony, welcoming 5–6,000 nurses from over 100 countries, is always an impressive occasion, but this time it held special meaning for some NCFI people, as Mo-Im Kim of Korea (jointly with Hildegard Peplau) was presented with the Christiane Reimann Award, ICN's highest honour; and Romania was received back into membership after more than fifty years, represented by Gabriela Bocec, a leader in Romanian nursing and in the national Romanian Nursing Association, and someone to whom NCFI meant very much. There has always been a number of Christians amongst the leaders of National Nursing Associations.

The NCFI stand in the exhibition was busy and just under two hundred people asked for more information. The NCFI Luncheon – where Tove Giske (Norway) spoke on 'Excellence in Clinical Practice', Lynda Miller (Canada), on 'Parish Nursing', and Harry Louden (General Director) on 'Leadership Development' – was attended by around 110 people, some of whom were not Christians.

A hospitality suite provided for NCFI in the hotel above the

Conference Centre, which was open from 1 p.m. to 7 p.m. each day, offered a restful place to meet, to talk, to pray, or just to drink coffee, eat, and enjoy each other's company. Nurses in many countries had, in the past, identified an ICN Congress as their first contact with NCFI, and this continued to be the case.

THE INTERNATIONAL BOARD

During the Hong Kong Conference in 1996 the International Forum had met, with twenty-three member countries represented, to consider the new structure and its implications, what it meant to be a member of NCFI, and to hear and consider reports from all the regions. Some of the news was encouraging, but financial and communication problems were still a challenge in some places, particularly in CAME and in Africa, where communication between countries might take three to four months. The International Board, with three members elected by each Regional Forum, had met only briefly, to elect the new NCFI President, Mary Thompson (USA), and Vice-President, Lili Makutu (Fiji), so that they could be announced before the end of the conference.

At the end of the conference the International Board met to begin for the first time its work as the regionally representative policy-making body of NCFI. This was a very important meeting, as the board was much larger than the previous executive, and would only be able to meet about every two years. (Even with the smaller number of members it had not always been possible to pay for attendance every time of all those Executive Committee members unable to fund their own travel to meetings.) Amongst their papers for the meeting, each person had a Board Member's job description. As President, Mary Thompson's gifts and skills, developed through experience as the Director of NCF USA, proved useful in helping board members to get to know each other better; identify their own gifts which could help in realising NCFI's long-term plan, and how they would like to be involved in board work; suggest others in their regions with particular gifts; set up prayer partnerships; and address the work of the board. This included reviewing the constitution and the guidelines for how individual Regions and NCFI as a whole would work together; strategies for assisting NNCFs, developing young leaders, and communication between Regions; financial issues and Regional responsibilities; and promoting countries' plans to celebrate NCFI's fortieth birthday in various ways – including giving to NCFI. Scottish, Finnish and Japanese proverbs were quoted in support of the view that everyone could contribute something, no gift was too small to matter.

Other matters for consideration included the reports and prayer requests of the General Director and two full-time Regional Co-ordinators (Eunice Siccardi – Latin America, and Micah Tswabki – Africa); plans for activities at the 1997 ICN Congress; the conference evaluations and suggestions for improvement next time; the need to update the *Conference Manual* started by Grace Wallace and Erna Goulding to assist host countries; and the location of NCFI Headquarters, since the lease of the present offices would soon expire. A Standing Committee was elected comprising the President (CANA), Vice-President (PACEA) and a member from each of the other four Regions. This committee would meet in the alternate years, when the board did not meet, and their work would include drawing up a budget, which would then need approval from the board.

Communication had always presented some problems in NCFI, whether they be geographical, technological or human (language differences could be one challenge, though there were others – a nurse leader once said we should pray that God would teach nurses in her region to write letters, which culturally they were not inclined to do!). The International Board would have more continuity than the CNR, but was much larger and would meet less frequently than the Executive Committee had, so good communication would be essential, but in some ways more difficult. The advent of email in the 1990s made a vast difference to the speed and convenience of communication, but only when a computer, electricity and a functional telephone line were available, which was not always so in Africa and in CAME, which also had the most postal difficulties.

For NCFI people passing through London, access to NCFI Headquarters had become easier – at the end of 1996 NCFI had moved to Maidstone into an office with two rooms which proved to be no more expensive than the single office held in Warrington. Maidstone is only around twenty miles from London, and is not far from main airports and Channel seaports. The move also meant that Harry Louden no longer had to spend four days a week away from home – his youngest daughter was in her final years at school in Maidstone, and his wife's work was there – while the Loudens' local church would provide support both to NCFI work and to Harry's wife and family while he was travelling.

NCFI owed a great debt of thanks to Stan Morris, who had voluntarily carried out the book-keeping and maintained the database for some years in Warrington, and who had showed very real support for, and interest in NCFI. The fact that his son lived in the London area, not far from Maidstone, made it easier for him to hand over to Bruce Corp, whose commitment and financial expertise as Financial Advisor proved a major blessing to NCFI as a result of the move.

The Standing Committee met in November 1997 and in January 1999, eleven members of the board, along with the General Director Harry Louden, met for a week in Kuala Lumpur, Malaysia. As usual the location had been chosen partly to minimise travel costs, and there was at least one board member present from each Region, with the exception of Latin America as Grace de Morillo was unable to be there (and without her translation skills, meetings in English only were a barrier to some).

In this case the meeting also preceded the PACEA Regional Committee, and Kuala Lumpur offered good facilities. The local NCF had secured hotel accommodation at extraordinarily reasonable cost, and the board members enjoyed the unusual luxury of a spacious meeting room located on the eighteenth floor, reached by a glass-sided lift, from which they enjoyed superb views when going to and from delicious meals, which prepared them well to work hard.

The Standing Committee had produced a paper on the Vision and Strategic Objectives of NCFI, and the board worked on developing a Long Range Plan, 1999–2003, with goals to achieve the objectives. Amongst other matters, thought was given, in the light of experience, to the orientation of new board members in 2000, and a binder of papers for them was suggested, and perhaps a 'buddy' system of new and old members. In earlier times, as with nursing, people had learned mainly by experience. Now that NCFI had developed so much over the years, there were many things, including relevant past papers, which committee members needed to know beforehand in order to function effectively and efficiently during meetings, and make the best use of time available.

In the evenings there were country reports and prayer, and in Harry Louden's report there was encouraging news – for example, of Ghana NCF's involvement in a Sickle Cell Disease Project; of Canada NCF using an unexpected gift to sponsor two Bolivian nurses allowing them to attend the Latin American NCFI Conference; of a post-graduate course in theology and health being developed in the USA; and of retired nurses there organising to support NCFI. But finance was still a concern; and after discussion on the need to communicate the vision, work and needs, on stewardship and how to find resources, board members for each Region decided what action they would take. During the meetings much thought and work was given to the next NCFI Conference which was to be held in Edinburgh, Scotland in 2000, and Evangeline Creighton was present with the board to help with this.

At the end of the board meetings, several members stayed to enjoy and contribute to the PACEA Regional Leadership days.

THE 2000 CONFERENCE – NCFI IN SCOTLAND

The fifteenth NCFI Conference took place from 3–10 July 2000 at the University of Edinburgh, with the theme 'Expanding the Horizons of Nursing: A Christian Perspective'. Over 300 nurses from around 40 countries enjoyed the hospitality of the Scots which was warm, even if the weather was not always so, and the facilities and green surroundings of the campus – also enjoyed by the wild rabbits!

Arrival had been preceded by months of preparation, not only in Edinburgh, but for many individuals elsewhere. As always, even before the many hours of travel to the conference there was for many participants the problem of obtaining visas, a process involving not only safe arrival of the necessary letter of invitation from the host country, but also money and sometimes travel of twelve or more hours to an embassy or consulate. One of the benefits of such conferences is a reminder, through hearing the experiences of others, of how much easier life is for some nurses than for others.

From 28 June to 2 July, there was a Leadership Conference which again had three tracks, but some sessions together. For 3 hours on each of the 3 afternoons, the newcomers and committee members/staff groups met to focus on different aspects of leadership and leadership training; while a third group of over 30 nurses from 14 countries in 5 Regions, followed the theme of 'Christ and Culture: Christian Scholarship and Nursing'. The varied presentations included some from areas of the world where nursing scholarship was well-developed, and one from a country where, due to its history, there was less experience in this respect.

In the main conference the Revd Dr Bruce Milne, a well-known Scottish theologian, gave the Bible expositions on the very practical themes of 'My Appreciation of God', 'My Relationship with God', 'My Love for Others', and 'Service and Stewardship of my Life'. Each was followed by short comments from a nurse respondent. Each day of the conference had as a theme one of the four main components identified in the NCFI Vision Statement where NCF could make a difference in nursing. Therefore the four professional plenary sessions were focused on 'The Knowledge Base of Nursing' (Judy Shelly and Arlene Miller, the USA); 'Leadership Development' (Eric Owusu, from Nigeria, and a post-graduate student in the UK); 'Global Collaboration' (Mary Thompson, USA, and Lili Makutu, Fiji) each of which were followed by discussion groups; and 'Being a Christian Voice in Nursing' (a panel of five nurses from five Regions, chaired by Harry Louden). The concurrent seminars provided choice in the afternoons. In the Conference Handbook Mary Thompson, President, had written,

> It [the conference] will be a time to recognise our Christian heritage in nursing … Our horizons will expand as we consider the future of nursing in the light of the gifts God has given us. We will also experience 'a taste of heaven' as we worship the Lord with people from around the world, and develop new international friendships.

The small groups and other sessions, mealtimes, outings and free time activities all contributed to this. The beauties of Loch Lomond, the Scottish countryside, the historic Blair Castle, and the Caithness Glass Centre were some of the attractions enjoyed by participants on the day out. But in the evening all were entertained by Harry Louden (a Scot in his tartan kilt) 'addressing the haggis' with Robert Burns poetry in traditional style, before the meal of 'haggis and neeps'. Scottish dancing in traditional dress followed, first performed expertly by a group, and then with varying degrees of expertise by the participants who joined in; a good example of the fun and fellowship so often found as part of NCFI events.

At the International Forum delegates from twenty-eight member countries (Ecuador, Israel, Liberia and Pakistan were not represented) heard the NCFI staff, President and Regions each report on their work. Eunice Siccardi, who had contributed immensely as an NCFI staff worker through the work in Latin America, and in Spain and NCFI generally since 1978, would finally retire at the end of the year. She had planned, with other leaders in Latin America, that co-ordination of the work in the Region would be shared between three volunteers, who would each work with a particular area. However Eunice would remain very much part of NCFI as she continued to orient and equip new volunteers (and would in 2004 become one of the International Board members for the Region.)

There was some encouraging news from all the regions, and many opportunities. But as Bruce Corp, voluntary Financial Advisor to NCFI, discussed the financial report given to delegates it was again evident that a regular committed income was needed. Expenses had been kept to a minimum, including not printing *CNI* when there was no money. But £20,000 (USD 32,000) was needed to cover the current deficit, £5,000 (USD 8,000) per month for the rest of the year, and £8,000 (USD 12,000) per month to cover needs in 2001. Suggestions were asked for and discussed. But as someone pointed out later, during discussion of the long range plan which was the framework for the future direction of NCFI, 'there was no clear indication of financial commitment / responsibility of Regions to NCFI' (International Forum

Minutes, 2000, 7).

The new International Board – with ten different members amongst the eighteen elected by the Regions, but the same President (Mary Thompson) and Vice-President (Lili Makutu) – would have more work to do on financial resources as well as moving forward in accord with the plans.

A NEW MILLENNIUM – THE FIRST FOUR YEARS

During this four years the work of NCFI, led by the board and staff (Harry Louden as General Director, and Micah Tswabki as Regional Co-ordinator for Africa), followed the current long-range plan. This had been developed over the past few years, reflecting the needs expressed by the NNCFs and those identified by NCFI staff and board members. The main elements were:

- Implement leadership development for the NCF International Board, staff, Regional and Country Committees that will equip them to fulfil NCF International vision in our six regions, member countries and contacts around the world
- Hold a worldwide NCFI conference in 2004 and Regional conferences in 2002, to prepare nurses to be a Christian voice in nursing and make Jesus Christ visible in their part of the world
- Produce resources to provide Biblical teaching, exchange of ideas, and to introduce and reinforce Christian beliefs and applications in nursing education, practice, management and research
- Provide a Christian presence and voice amongst nursing leaders around the world through involvement with national and international professional meetings and strategies, to influence the direction of nursing
- Mobilise leaders from member countries and regions, to provide partnerships to strengthen global influence of NCF International

- Facilitate a network of practical caring for nurses as caregivers within the NCFI family, to demonstrate our caring Christian values
- Expand prayer and financial support for the NCF International ministry, to deepen foundations for Christian witness and influence in nursing for the twenty-first century

NCFI leadership materials developed for conferences and leadership training were in use in several regions. These were revised for the 2004 conference and included content on cross-cultural communication. The board again sought to collect information about other relevant resources available in Regions and NNCFs and encourage exchange where this could prove useful.

However, one important resource had been lost. The Spanish edition of *CNI*, first produced for the ICN Conference in Madrid 1993, proved too expensive by the late 1990s. A survey by the new editor in 1998 showed that the journal itself was much appreciated around the world, but by 2000 it was decided that it could no longer be published unless a subscription list adequate to make it financially viable could be developed. Such a publication had always cost NCFI money, because in so many countries nurses could not afford to buy it at a realistic price. Occasionally an issue could not be published because of lack of funds, which meant adjusting subscription duration so that subscribers received what they had paid for. But *Highway* (and later *CNI*) had been recognised as a vital means of communication, and had developed into a journal which could take its place in nursing libraries alongside other professional publications. Now it would have to be replaced by a short and cheaper publication twice a year, *NCFI Link International*, containing news, information, book reviews and sometimes letters, or one or two short articles.

There also continued to be a three-monthly *Prayer Guide*, in addition to an 'emergency prayer network', used when some NCFI person or situation urgently required prayer. *The Journal of Christian Nursing* (*JCN*), published by NCF USA, was a useful resource for others too, but for some time there had been discussion of the need for a scholarly international Christian nursing journal, possibly edited by

Judy Shelly, who edited *JCN*. Bart Cusveller, a nurse on the staff of a Christian College in the Netherlands, later agreed to take this idea forward, however no such new journal has proved possible so far (though there have been occasional issues of *CNI*, such as the one for the 2008 NCFI Fiftieth Anniversary Conference).

One highlight of this period was the 2001 ICN Congress held in Copenhagen, Denmark. The NCFI stand in the exhibition was busy as usual, but this time there was also a symposium on 'Spiritual Care', as part of the main ICN programme of concurrent sessions. This had been planned well in advance, organised by Tove Giske (Norway) with other NCFI people who had done work on spiritual care, and the proposal submitted had been accepted.

An interesting ICN plenary session was given by a French psychiatrist, who was the first to go round the world non-stop in a hot-air balloon. He talked about the importance of realising that to make good progress it was necessary to find and use skilfully the most advantageous air currents, at different levels. The balloon's progress in speed and direction was dependent on these currents, which could not be controlled, but could be found and used. He indicated that he sometimes talked to his patients about life being like that. Circumstances cannot always be controlled by humans, but available resources can be used to improve the outcomes. This proved to be a very relevant message, remembered by at least one nurse involved when NCFI faced a major crisis four years later and, with God's guidance, was seeking the way forward.

Then there were the Regional Conferences, always vital in giving newcomers an experience of the NCFI family as well as supporting, re-energising and developing those who had already 'caught the vision'. Harry Louden, General Director, had been able to take part in three such events – the PACEA Conference held in the Philippines; CAME in Bangladesh (which became a member in 1999); and Europe, where a number of nurses from Eastern Europe were among conference participants. Despite limited resources, Harry had also visited Papua New Guinea and India for their national conferences, Hong Kong for the PACEA staff retreat, the USA for the 2002 Board Meeting, Korea, Malaysia, Singapore, and Thailand. There had been many opportunities to do leadership training, lead Bible studies, and speak on various issues. At the request of the European promoter of Healthcare (formerly Hospital) Christian Fellowship International (HCFI), with whom he had had contact earlier, he visited the staff worker and the Bangkok Christian Hospital. Since the separation in 1967, when HCFI officially came into being, HCFI and NCFI were, at least initially, supposed to be working in different countries. NCFI's proposal of co-operation and exchange of information did not appear to be implemented much. In the intervening years some NNCFs had experienced problems with HCFs, and sought help from NCFI. The policy developed by NCFI had been to encourage recognition of the different aims of HCFI, including its focus on evangelising patients; to encourage NCFs to work alongside HCFs where both existed, and allow dual membership (except for NCF leaders). By the early years of the twenty-first century, most of the people involved in the 1967 division were no longer around, and the HCFI leader in the Netherlands, which had always been a main focus in addition to South Africa, appeared to be seeking better and closer relationships with NCFI.

Several significant matters addressed by the board during this time merit comment. One was the request from Colombia that NCFI should support the proposal within WHO that spiritual aspects should be included in the WHO definition of health. Further work was done on proposed wording of such a definition, and in 2001 NCF Colombia (through Marina Navarette and Grace de Morillo) and NCFI (through Mary Thompson and Judy Shelly), put forward the definition: 'Health is a dynamic state of physical, mental, spiritual and social well-being, and not merely the absence of disease and infirmity.' This was sent in a letter to WHO in 2001, with good arguments for adopting it. When the reply made clear that a proposal could only be accepted from country members of the General Assembly, Norway NCF contacted their Minister of Health, and had a positive response. Other members of the Board were encouraged to seek the support of their governments, and ask their colleagues in the WHO Collaborating Centres for Nursing in other countries to do the same. However change in the definition of health remained an ongoing and unresolved issue in WHO for some years.

Another issue was the addition at the 2002 Board Meeting of a new objective to the NCFI long-range plan, which arose from a comment by Loice Chipere (Zambia) in discussion on fund-raising, which remained important to support the ongoing work. She said NCFI seemed to be reaching people at an intellectual level, and perhaps if there was also more tangible support for nurses (for example, providing equipment) this might encourage others to give. The objective proposed and accepted by the Board was, 'To facilitate a global network of practical caring for nurses as caregivers within the NCFI family.' This would be taken forward within the Regions.

Often trustees tend to work in the background almost unnoticed, but the NCFI trustees and their work were on the board agenda in 2000. For over twenty years the three NCFI trustees had been Evangeline Creighton, Ruth Lichtenberger and Pat Ashworth. As General Director and past Presidents they all had been very involved in the work but until 2000 had rarely met as trustees; and Ruth had ceased to be a trustee as her life developed in other areas. However NCFI's registration as a UK charity, which offers tax benefits, means that it is subject to the relevant legislation, and by the year 2000 requirements from the Charity Commission were changing, necessitating more formal function of the Trustees. In future they would meet at least annually and would provide formal reports, and it was decided again to try to increase the number of trustees. This had not proved easy in the past, as they must not only be suitable people from an NCFI perspective, but also UK citizens, and are legally responsible for ensuring that NCFI meets requirements as a charity, and are personally liable for any debts it cannot pay. David Parfitt had been familiar with NCFI for some time as his wife Barbara had been involved for a number of years, including being a member of the European Regional Committee and the International Board. He became a trustee in 2002; but at that time Evangeline Creighton resigned due to health and other reasons. The role of NCFI trustees in the twentieth century had been mainly relatively passive – more of a safety net – but was to become more active and significant, particularly in 2004–5.

THE 2004 CONFERENCE – NCFI IN KOREA

More than 350 nurses from 28 nations gathered at the NCFI Conference in Korea, held from 4–9 July 2004 in the Seoul Olympic Parktel – a hotel located in the pleasant open park which had been home to the Olympic Games in 1988. Seoul itself is a city both ancient and very modern with a population of around 11 million people.

At the NCFI Opening Ceremony the keynote address was given by Dr Mo-Im Kim, a distinguished Korean Christian nurse, whose long career included becoming a ICN President, winning the Christiane Reimann Award, and being Minister of Health of her own country. The overall conference theme was 'Challenged to Care: a Christian Perspective to Nursing', and the daily expositions on the Biblical base of caring were provided by Kamalini Kumar (India/the USA), Anne Workman Hawes (Canada), and Micah Tswabki (Nigeria), all nurses well-qualified to integrate Biblical and nursing knowledge. Their sessions, and the professional plenary sessions which followed, were each in accord with the theme for the day. The four themes and speakers for the professional sessions were: 'Care for the Caregiver' (Susie Kim, Korea); 'Social and Political Impact of Globalization' (Barbara Parfitt, UK); 'Paradigm Shift in Nursing Practice' (Judy Shelly, the USA); and 'Celebrating Diversity' (a panel made up of one representative from each Region, led by Kamalini Kumar). The specially prepared 'Quiet time/ Devotional Guide', a feature of all the NCFI Conferences since its early days, also followed the theme for the day, and as always the worship led by different people provided reflection, inspiration and joyful expression. Again there was a Leadership Track and a Scholarship Track, and a glance at the abstracts shows a wide variety of seminars and papers addressing practical and academic issues.

Celebrating cultural diversity was not, of course, confined to the academic programme. On Sunday those who chose to were 'shepherded' to church by volunteers from NCF Korea, which had also provided as a gift to all participants the umbrellas which sheltered them from the pouring rain! For at least some who attended Yoido Full Gospel Church, worshipping with so many thousands of people packed into the vast church, for one of about seven Sunday services, was a memorable experience even before the conference began. There were opportunities for hospital visits and, on Wednesday afternoon, optional visits to Gyeongbok Palace, Biwon Garden, or the Korean Folk Village. Despite the persistent rain (the umbrellas proved useful again!) there were many interesting things to see and learn about, and in the evening even the rain could not interfere with enjoyment of the good food, colourful and beautiful national dresses, and other cultural pleasures provided by NCF Korea.

As always the 'Country Sharing' evenings and exhibition were an important part of the conference, and the Attendance Certificate, surrounded by photos from the conference, would provide evidence for the continuing educational purposes of participating in an academic Christian conference. But just as important (or perhaps even more so) are the memories, learning and perhaps other changes which participants took home with them – memories such as five room-mates from various countries performing a Bangladeshi dance in appropriate dress (much enjoyed by the Romanian member of the dance group); Korean children peeping round the door to watch the Fijians dancing; the delight of six nurses from China openly participating in the conference; many of the participants walking round the room with hands linked, singing 'We are walking in the light of God' at the end of the conference; and other more serious memories which would strengthen, support and perhaps change their Christian lives back at home, in very different circumstances.

During the conference each Regional Forum had met to consider its past and future work and elect its International Board Members. By 2002 the Regions had or were developing Regional long-range plans with objectives, and Europe had, with its 'Strategic Plan and Objectives', an action plan with target dates. (NCFI has always benefited from the expertise leaders in the profession brought to it from their daily work, as well as helping nurses contribute what they have learned through NCF/NCFI to the profession.)

The International Forum also met to learn more about progress and consider NCFI's work, receiving a PowerPoint presentation of the Regional Reports, written reports from the President and the General

Director, and a paper on the 2001–2005 long-range plan. This showed the seven components, each with associated objectives, and the progress made (by July 2004) on achieving them. All these reports contained some encouraging news of an active, and in some respects growing, organisation.

However the Financial Report was less encouraging. Despite a matching grant of USD $20,000 obtained by one of the board members in 2001, and a legacy of £18,000 in 2003, the report stated 'Financial position remains fragile'. A paper presented at the forum described how this had been addressed so far. At the 2002 meeting the board had again discussed the need for sufficient funding not only to sustain NCFI, but to enable it to develop and make an impact in the future, and to achieve its aims. So while recognising some increase in income and the commitment of many NNCFs to NCFI, the board charged each Region to consult its members on the proposal that:

> Regional and national groups, who make up the membership of NCFI, will financially support the organisation. The level of support will be calculated proportionally according to the GDP of each region. The amount identified will reflect the individual economic status of the regional membership.

This formalised an idea that had been discussed intermittently, and did not suggest that the proportional contribution would be a formal subscription, but it would informally 'represent an equivalent level of commitment'. Feedback from the Regional consultations, formal and informal, was that the members fully recognised the need for sustainable funding for development, and for NCFI to implement modern working practices equal to other professional organisations, while not losing the caring spirit and promotion of the Christian dimension of practice. 'Prayer and faith are the foundations of the membership. However the overall view of the membership is that they do not support the proposal as set out by the board.' The forum was therefore asked to consider and recommend one of three other alternatives – a membership fee for each country (reflecting the average salary and number of members in the country); each member country to commit to donating a minimum of 10 per cent of their NNCF income to NCFI; or each country to decide an amount which they would covenant to give annually – and also to comment on other suggested means of raising funds. The Finance Committee were later to work on the outcomes of the discussion.

After the conference the new board met on two days, with eight new members (though one had been on NCFI staff and another on the Executive Committee), a new President – Kamalini Kumar (India and the USA), and a new Vice-President – Sam Mbok (Nigeria). The manual for new board members was distributed, and in highlighting the responsibilities and position description of a Board Member, the President emphasised that 'This is a policy-making and decision-making, but mainly a *working* board.' Each member would be responsible for helping their region to accomplish the goals, for communicating adequately, and for sending the General Director the annual report for the Region; and also for fund-raising, though their personal and financial sacrifice was recognised. (Most were still self-funded when organising travel to and accommodation at meetings etc.) As the meeting proceeded, it was agreed that each Region would develop a formal list of people with expertise who could be used as a resource in NCFI; the Seoul Conference was reviewed and considered successful; and it was confirmed that Nigeria should host the next conference in 2008 (if the criteria from 2000/2002 Boards were met).

By the end of the meeting the board had appointed a sub-committee – who would ascertain the feasibility of maintaining an office in England (because of costs) – the Finance Committee, and the Standing Committee (which would also be the Conference Committee). It also had an action plan and list of board responsibilities for the coming years, including items to be followed up by the General Director, and had planned a meeting of the Standing/Conference Committee in Abuja in 2005. But human plans do not always work out; some things were soon to change.

A MAJOR CRISIS – AND OPPORTUNITY

Throughout NCFI's existence, faith had always been essential in dealing with financial matters. Nurses generally are not amongst the most highly paid in any society, and in many countries their salaries have remained extremely low, or even not been paid at all at some times. The staff and Executive Committee of NCFI had often worked and prayed long and hard to set budgets and make resources stretch as far as possible to meet the needs perceived, or expressed by the NNCFs or nurses in other countries. God had provided, through individuals, through NNCFs and occasionally through missionary societies or other foundations. NCFI had been blessed with faithful and experienced fund-raisers such as Grace Wallace and Mary Thompson in the USA and others, some of whom had to find creative ways of overcoming economic problems and currency restrictions in some countries; and with advice and help from a few non-nurses with financial expertise. Much had been achieved with very limited amounts of money. But in 1998 Ruth Lichtenberger, ex-General Director, wrote in an article celebrating forty years of NCFI,

> Will we celebrate fifty years? At a time when hundreds of nurses in Eastern Europe are looking to neighbouring NNCFs and NCF International, NCFI is having one of the most difficult times in its history. Financially it feels as if the well has run dry ... NCFI is challenged to remember that God has called us into being, has been our provider in the past and is still our greatest resource. We look to Him in prayer to move nurses around the world to share in the cost of maintaining NCFI staff, facilities and ministries ... NCFI is alive and well and continues to have a vital ministry in the encouragement of nurses' fellowships and the maintenance of Christian principles in nursing.
> (Lichtenberger, 1998, 11)

In the first few years of the new century, income from giving remained less than necessary, reserves from the earlier sale of the Penge property had all been used, and NCFI survived financially only with a tax rebate from the conference in 2000, a one-off matching grant and a legacy. Repeatedly Bruce Corp, NCFI Financial Advisor, warned in his regular reports that, while recognising dependence on God, NCFI could not responsibly continue as it was without more regular income.

The 2004 Conference had been planned to result in income but –

because the firm Global Conference Planning, Korean NCF and NCFI HQ were all involved – it was not until November 2004 that it became evident that there would be a large deficit, due to the firm being unable to obtain expected sponsorship, and other unexpected costs related to some participants. This, plus the already inadequate income, meant that by the end of the year NCFI would be functioning but unable to pay its bills, which would be illegal under British charity law; and the trustees could be taken to court and have to pay the money owed, which the Finance Committee considered unacceptable.

It was evident that a crisis point had been reached and, with sadness, the trustees, with the NCFI President and Finance Committee of the board, made the decision to close down the NCFI office in Maidstone and cease to employ the General Director, Harry Louden. However all, including the rest of the board members, recognised that this would not be the end of NCFI, since it was obvious that God was still working through it and there was still much to do. It was encouraging that, when the Christian Medical Fellowship in the UK, with which there had always been a good relationship, heard the news they promptly offered any possible help, for example with administrative matters such as mailshots.

Harry Louden had been the General Director for nearly ten years, and had achieved a lot with limited financial resources. Much of his travel around the world had been through creative use of offers such as those of firms to conference organisers, at little cost to NCFI. Many nurses and NNCFs had benefited from his teaching on the Bible, leadership or other issues at conferences. He had made contacts in other countries, and also with the ICN Director and with WHO in Geneva, as well as the ongoing communication and work with committees and NCFI in general. Despite his absence while travelling and intermittent financial uncertainty, his wife, Ruth, and their family and church had supported him in his work with NCFI. He would be missed in NCFI, but God had led him into NCFI work and would lead him back into nursing, to serve amongst nurses in a different way.

At this time there were only two trustees, David Parfitt and Pat Ashworth, and to them fell the task of closing down the Maidstone

NCFI office. God had provided the complementary knowledge and experience of, in David, a professional administrator and husband of an NCFI Board member, who though not currently in a post, had experience of this kind of activity; and, in Pat, a nurse who had been involved with NCFI in various ways since 1964.

Both lived almost five hundred miles away from Maidstone, in Scotland and Northern Ireland respectively, so the work had to be compressed into visits of two to three days. One concentrated most on the administrative process of closing the office and preserving the recent financial and other ongoing records, while the other worked through reports, letters and other papers, photos/slides, and all the other things from forty-six years of operation which were in the packed storage areas, to try to make sure that nothing essential to NCFI's history, as well as future, would be lost.

God's work through NCFI lives on in people throughout the world, but since most of us do not have the strong oral tradition of some cultures, much of NCFI's history (and that of NNCFs) may be lost as the years pass, unless it is preserved and recorded; and our history is part of our identity, as well as giving a sense of perspective in both good and difficult times.

News of the financial problems, and updates on further news, had been sent to board members and to NNCFs and others around the world. Prayers were answered as some NNCFs and individuals, particularly NCF USA, gave extra gifts; and by March 2005 debts were paid, the Maidstone NCFI office had closed down, and NCFI had a new temporary location in the home of the Parfitts in Scotland.

At this point NCFI regretfully lost its Financial Advisor, Bruce Corp, who had taken on this work at the request of Harry Louden. His financial expertise, experience and faithful work over the years in Maidstone had been much appreciated, and his clear financial statements and sound Christian advice had been essential for those involved in NCFI work. Now he resigned, but God had prepared his successor.

NCFI was still very much alive. Many nurses had gone from the 2004 NCFI Conference challenged, but encouraged, with renewed energy and commitment. To quote examples from one of Mary Thompson's regular NCFI prayer and fund-raising letters, November 2004,

> NCF in Hong Kong and Malaysia held retreats for leaders following the NCFI Conference. The Fellowship of Christian Nurses in Nigeria had a national conference in September, over 750 nurses and students attended. NCF leaders from Japan, Philippines and Singapore extended God's care through travelling to Indonesia to assist the newly forming NCF movement.

Over eighty nurses were at those meetings, but equally important were the many others around the world encouraged in working faithfully to 'make a difference', often in difficult circumstances. So why, when God had provided just enough for NCFI to move forward with good stewardship for so many years, had He allowed the crisis to happen? Perhaps it was a necessary stimulus for NCFI to move on to its next major stage of development.

6

2005 AND BEYOND — AN INTEGRATED
REGION-BASED ORGANISATION

WHAT NEXT? — BEGINNING ANOTHER NEW ERA

The world in general, and the world of nursing, nurses and NCFI, had changed in significant ways over the almost fifty years since the first meeting in Keswick to discuss the formation of such a Fellowship. Increases in availability of television, cheaper, quicker air travel, and developments in communication such as fax and email had increased awareness of what was happening in other countries and made contacts and communication between many nurses easier.

Changes in nursing in a number of countries had increased nurses' independence in thought and action, and given more nurse leaders experience of functioning in international organisations. Of course NCFI always has to recognise that in many countries nursing salaries are still comparatively low, communications still difficult and relatively slow, and opportunities for development in nursing less. It is necessary to make allowance for such factors, and try to help overcome the problems so that NNCFs in all countries can play their full part in the Fellowship, both in contributing and receiving. But by 2005 the International Board comprising elected representatives of the six NCFI Regions – Africa, CAME, CANA, Europe, Latin America, and PACEA – was providing opportunity and encouragement for leaders in each Region to meet (not always easy within some Regions) and think and plan regionally as well as globally. All Regions were functioning to some extent, though some with more difficulty or more activity than others, and with varying numbers of member countries (CANA still had only the USA and Canada, while PACEA had nine member countries). Despite changes in individual countries, the challenges faced in the Regions were still similar in many respects to those described earlier, some shared with other Regions and some different. This was the situation in early 2005, as the board became the leadership of NCFI which was now without a General Director, or any other staff, except for Micah Tswabki as Regional Co-ordinator in Africa. The board and NCFI Regions were ready for a new challenge in a modern world with available technology.

At this critical point for NCFI it was essential for the full International Board to meet, together with the trustees and Mary Thompson (the immediate past President), to pray, discuss and find together the way forward for NCFI, and make plans for progress. As a board member had said in an email during the financial crisis, 'We as an organisation are reflecting what is going on all over the world. May the Lord grant His wisdom in the next steps to take.' All were convinced that NCFI was very much alive and necessary; only the Maidstone office had closed. The crisis in 2004 could be God's way of moving NCFI into exciting new developments. There was a reminder that the future would be built on sound foundations from the past, as it was a legacy from Margaret Smith, the first full-time Secretary to NCFI in the 1960s, which provided the necessary funds for the full Board Meeting instead of the planned Standing Committee (only four board members were not able to be present, and these absences were not for financial reasons).

The meeting was held from 3–6 July 2005, at Kilcreggan, a Christian guesthouse overlooking Loch Fyne in southern Scotland – a beautiful and peaceful place, ideal for such an occasion. As always, the meeting began with worship. Then progress on business ongoing from the previous board was reviewed, and the trustees described reasons for the changes in NCFI. Appreciation was expressed for the contributions to NCFI of Harry Louden, previously General Director, and Bruce Corp, Financial Advisor; and also for offers of help by the Christian Medical Fellowship (CMF) whose staff member for Allied Health Professions, Steve Fouch, had been invited and was present for the early part of the meeting.

So how would NCFI continue to work in the future? Those present turned to this important question, working through mixed Regional brain-storming in small groups, and discussion all together, resulting in the following major decisions. It was agreed that NCFI would have a flat, decentralised structure, with the Regions collaborating, and the Board making a strategic plan based on the needs expressed through the Regions. The Regional strategic aims to be achieved would be:

- Training and education – achieved with workshops and Biblical teaching
- Development and Expansion – supporting and encouraging existing NNCFs, developing new NNCFs and increasing membership and activities
- Practical Caring (Service) – projects and caring activities (with one another and working in the community)

These aims and associated objectives would be discussed with Regions by their own committees, which would both feed back information to the board and each make and implement a plan for their own Region. It was recognised as the responsibility of all Regions and NNCFs to raise funds for NCFI, for Regional activities, and sponsorship as necessary for attendance at international meetings and conferences. Many people paid for themselves, but where this was not possible, those who needed sponsorship would be expected to find at least part of the cost themselves. It might be possible in the future to provide some support for individual Regional Projects.

The administrative work of NCFI taken on by David Parfitt, with the office in the Parfitts' home, was much appreciated, and he agreed to continue this, though it would have to remain voluntary work until more trustees were appointed, and he could resign from being one. (This became possible during the following year, when he became officially employed as part-time Administrator for ten hours per week.) The Finance Committee was joined by a new Financial Advisor – John White. A certified public accountant in the USA, with a special interest in NCFI work through his wife, Barbara White, who was a board member, John was present throughout the week to contribute advice on future financial arrangements.

Communication would remain of crucial importance, both between board members and to the wider network. Email proved invaluable both for board and Regional work, and for sending out the three-monthly *Prayer Guide*. It was also planned to continue the previous *Link* publication in a cheaper way.

The position of Micah Tswabki as Regional Co-ordinator for Africa was considered no longer feasible with the restructuring. He had served his own NNCF as a staff worker in Nigeria and taken on the work of co-ordination in the Region, and in 1993 had been appointed as Regional Co-ordinator with the full agreement of the African NNCFs. Travelling in difficult and sometimes dangerous circumstances, he had worked with active NCFs in African Member Countries of NCFI and also made or followed up contacts in a number of non-member African countries. These included Tanzania, Kenya, Ethiopia, Uganda, Niger, Cameroon, and Botswana, as well as Liberia and Sierra Leone, which had previously been visited by Mary Aboagye. His teaching and quiet leadership were much appreciated not only in Africa, but also by nurses from many countries through his participation in international conferences. Support from his wife, Esther, no doubt added strength for his service, though his absences while travelling must have added challenges to bringing up their six children so successfully. Problems in obtaining visas, and with other aspects of travel, and difficulties in communication because of unreliable telephone and electricity services, had made it increasingly difficult to function internationally from his location in Wukari, Northern Nigeria. Micah had followed God's leading to become 'Father Africa' as the Regional Co-ordinator, and after 2005 would leave NCFI staff and have more time for his work serving God as a church pastor, though FCN (the Nigerian NCF) would no doubt continue to benefit from his wisdom and experience.

MOVING ON

Conferences remain an important means of making NCFI known, helping nurses to catch a vision of what could be achieved, and helping them to work towards it.

Nurses only really begin to understand what it means to be part of the NCFI family when they experience living, worshipping, working and recreation together with nurses from many other countries. The

ICN Conference in Taiwan 2005 occurred just as NCFI was in the midst of change, and there was no formal representation of NCFI there. However a number of NCFI people were there and able to enjoy contact.

By this time ICN had begun to hold a conference in conjunction with each biennial Council of National Representatives meeting (already held about mid-point between the larger Quadrennial Conferences); and in 2007, in Yokohama, Japan, and in co-operation with NCF Japan, NCFI again had an exhibition stand and representation. Many contacts were made with 'old friends' and nurses who did not know of NCFI, including Mongolian nurses who already had a Christian Nurses Fellowship. The exhibition panel illustrating Spiritual Care based on a Biblical perspective interested many students and nurses, including some Japanese nurse educators who said they were not Christian but 'this makes sense'. Three of them asked for someone from NCF Japan to visit them for follow-up meetings. There were also two seminars on 'Servant Leadership' by Barbara White (an NCFI Board Member), one of which was held for NCF Japan and lasted for a full day after the conference. As always, those working through NCFI enjoyed fellowship with each other and the hosts (in this case NCF Japan), learned, broadened their vision and gained confidence.

It had been planned for some years that the 2008 conference marking the fiftieth anniversary of NCFI's formal constitution would be in Nigeria, as there had been no global NCFI conference in Africa since 1976. Nigeria had had a strong NCF for many years, but it took time to confirm that there would be no insuperable visa or other problems, and to decide a suitable and economically possible location so it was not until 2007 that the location was confirmed as Jos, Northern Nigeria. The theme chosen was 'Strengthened to Serve: Christian Response to Global Health Needs', a theme which indicates two things. First, that health needs in one part of the world affect and may quickly appear in others, even if they are not yet evident; and second, that there are relevant responses which Christians should be making, whatever the health needs are and wherever help is needed to meet them, and usually that help includes nursing.

WHAT HAS NCFI CONTRIBUTED TO NURSES AND NURSING?

As a Christian organisation NCFI's most important functions are, of course (from a Christian perspective), to help nurses to develop a personal faith in and relationship with God in accord with the Basis of Faith, and to help them to practise that faith in their lives and profession. This has been done through supporting existing and developing NNCFs, or individual nurses where there was no NCF, through conferences or other education, printed resources such as Bible study guides or other literature linking faith with practice, through news and prayer networks, and personal contacts or visits. It is not possible to know how many nurses' lives have been influenced or even totally changed by God in ways which were stimulated by contact with NCFI, though it is known that many have. But there are other contributions which NCFI has made, and still makes, to nursing which can be recognised as beneficial from any perspective, not only a Christian one. Some of these are as follows.

Cultural knowledge and sensitivity

NCFI conferences and some other NCFI events provide opportunities for developing cultural knowledge and sensitivity. There, nurses from many nations and cultures meet, live, learn, work and have fun together, developing understanding and acceptance of each other's differences, as well as similarities. The atmosphere of acceptance based on belief that each person is of equal value, and recognition that all can both contribute to and learn something from others, provides a 'safe space'. Such experiences help to develop nurses who have the motivation, understanding and ability to respect and work well with people wherever they come from; and these are valuable qualities in a world of global travel and migration, where in many countries both healthcare staff and those who need healthcare may come from a variety of countries and cultures.

Leadership

From early in its existence NCFI has provided teaching on leadership, and still does so, both in teaching sessions and through involving nurses in leadership with experienced leaders – learning by example and by doing. This is an important service in a world where nurses able to lead in nursing are needed, where the vast majority of nurses in most countries are women, and where many countries and cultures have been slow to encourage or even allow women leaders. Moreover, the kind of leadership taught – servant leadership encouraging and enabling those led to develop their full potential and provide the best possible care and service to patients or others who need it – is the kind of leadership needed in healthcare (and elsewhere). This is more likely to lead to the best use of limited resources and happier, more productive staff than when leaders are focused on personal status, ambition and dominance.

Commitment to professional development and continued learning

Many nurses have been stimulated through NCFI events to develop commitment to professional development and continued learning, and have been helped to achieve it, in a Christian context. From the first NCFI involvement at ICN Congress in 1965 (or perhaps even before this) NCFI leaders have demonstrated their commitment to involvement in the profession of nursing as a vocation. NCFI conferences include content which builds up both Christian knowledge and commitment and also professional knowledge, good practice, and the ability to address professional issues. Over the years the academic level in NCFI events has risen, as it has in nursing generally, but always with the aim to make material accessible also to those nurses with fewer educational opportunities available in their countries. The formal and informal exchange of information, knowledge, ideas and sometimes wisdom between nurses relatively highly privileged in terms of higher education in nursing and healthcare resources, and those facing much greater challenges due to economic, political, geographical and sometimes religious factors, can benefit all those involved.

Challenges faced in nursing in one country may be similar, though perhaps in a different form, to those facing nurses in other parts of the world, currently or in the future. Material on spiritual care or ethics, written by Christian nurses in the USA, Europe or elsewhere can be useful to nurses and improve care in other parts of the world, if used in a culturally sensitive way. Hearing about nursing situations in places such as Africa, countries in the CAME, Latin American and parts of the PACEA Regions can provoke reflection, different perspectives and challenge in nurses in other places, including those with the ability and opportunities to write and publish. Always within NCFI, the NNCFs, and the individuals which constitute them, the aim of education, scholarship and professional development is nurses who 'serve the Lord with heart and soul and *mind*,' in providing better healthcare for all, rather than only for status and salary. (Though both of these are legitimate benefits which may enable people to serve better.)

An international network

An international network, such as NCFI, of nurses in many countries who know each other, and have or can easily make personal contacts, can be valuable and enjoyable. This has always been important so that nurses can learn from each other, help, support and share their resources, including praying for each other with understanding. In earlier years when international travel and communication were slower and more difficult, and fewer nurses had international connections, such networks were important. Now for many nurses travel and communication are easier, and professional networks more common. But the NCFI network is still important, particularly since many nurses must leave home to work or study abroad for economic or other reasons, and need local help and support. In 1999 Lynaugh and Brush wrote, 'Despite wars, political and economic chaos and racial and religious strife the International Council of Nurses had been held together ...

by a "special glue" concocted by dedicated nurses. Its ingredients – friendship, collegial support and enthusiasm.' (Lynaugh and Brush, 1999, 3)

This has been true of nurses in NCFI, but with the additional benefits of shared faith and trust in the love, grace and power of one God, the Father, Son and Holy Spirit. (While many nurses in ICN were or are Christian, of course not all are.)

Nursing scholarship and spiritual care in nursing

NCFI has facilitated contributions to nursing scholarship and dissemination of ideas, particularly in the area of spiritual care in nursing. Christian nurses have done academic studies on spiritual care and/or written books and articles in professional journals on it in the USA, the UK, Scandinavia, Taiwan and elsewhere; and through NCFI they have met, exchanged and developed their knowledge and ideas. Through presentations and feedback at NCFI conferences they have learned more about cultural differences, and giving and teaching spiritual care in different cultural, political, religious and economic situations. Spiritual aspects of care have become recognised as important in many countries and at global level, for example in the World Health Organisation, though what the term means is interpreted in some very different ways.

Helping nurses to grow to a mature Christian faith

But the most important contribution of NCFI and the NNCFs which constitute it remains that of helping nurses to come to and/or develop a personal knowledge of and relationship with God the Father, Son Jesus Christ, and Holy Spirit, and grow to a mature Christian faith. Wherever they work nurses may face great and sometimes apparently insurmountable challenges, with many physical and emotional demands from people with great nursing needs, and too little staff, equipment, and other resources to meet them, and often lack of support and understanding from those who manage and control resources. Of course there are everywhere some nurses to whom nursing is merely a job, a way of earning a living; but for most it is more than that and they want to do good work.

Perhaps one of the greatest challenges good, committed nurses face generally is discouragement – a sense of failure when going off duty, feeling that despite working hard it has been impossible to provide the good nursing care they wanted to give, and that their patients needed; and starting the next shift still carrying the burden of guilt from the last one. This can be as true in so-called developed countries where there are more resources, but also higher expectations, as it is in places with far fewer resources. But for Christian nurses who commit their lives to following Jesus Christ, wherever they are and whatever the demands and expectations there is a difference. They know their human limitations, that God is in control, and provides help to supplement human efforts to fulfil His plans; that as each day's (or night's) work ends they can thank God for His help in what has been achieved and commit the work to Him, ask forgiveness for any failures of theirs, and after rest and prayer begin a new shift, unburdened by guilt from the previous one.

Christian nurses therefore have hope, not only for life after death but for this life too; and hope which sustains committed, competent, compassionate nursing practice makes a great contribution in any nursing team in any area of practice and the world, and so to the healthcare people need. NNCFs and NCFI help nurses to find and sustain that hope, and the faith on which it is based, and share it.

LOOKING TO THE FUTURE – THE NEXT FIFTY YEARS

In celebrating forty years Ruth Lichtenberger, previously NCF General Director, considered the apparent gap between needs and resources and questioned, 'Will we celebrate fifty years?' The answer is 'Yes'. In September 2008, at the NCFI Fiftieth Anniversary Conference held in Jos, Nigeria, there was great celebration, praise and thanks to God by around 350 Africans and 104 nurses from elsewhere; and also by nurses in many other parts of the world.

It is impossible to know what will happen in the future, but it is possible to make some estimates, based on what is known so far. Already PACEA, the first NCFI Region to be defined, is leading the way with a Regional project (with Philippine and Indonesian missions as partners) to help Indonesian nurses and the embryo NNCF there by 'Training Trainers' and through several workshops. The project, led by Alicia Banas (Philippines), Swee Eng Goh (Singapore) and Chieko Fukushima (Japan), will help to establish a church-based primary healthcare education for lay people in three places in Indonesia. Work by Ghana NNCF, related to AIDS, may be developed by the African Region; and the European Region is considering work with migrating nurses, many of whom leave home to work in countries where conditions in nursing are better, but the nurses may arrive as strangers and face difficulties. Europe includes countries from which many nurses leave and also countries which receive them. The PACEA Project has been granted a contribution from NCFI for partnership funding, and NCFI is open to applications from other regions for this kind of assistance, as funds allow.

Planning for future Regional Conferences is also in progress. Such gatherings are important for nurses to 'catch the vision', develop it further together, and go home better equipped to work towards making it reality. But travel is costly, and NCFI leaders are already doing some committee and other work through modern technology such as email and conference phone calls.

No doubt nursing will change at least as much in the next fifty years as it did in the past, and probably NCFI will too. But the basic needs of human beings for physical, psychological, social and spiritual health do not appear to change much, though there may be superficial differences in the way they appear and are met – or not met. People will always need nurses as long as nurses provide help in meeting those needs, and nurses will always need support and help to meet their own needs. Around the world there are places where NCFs are growing and/

or making a difference, sometimes despite great difficulties, as well as there being some places where NCFs have become less active and perhaps nurses are in need of more support. Within NCFI their joys and sorrows, struggles and successes, and needs and faith are shared, and resources combined to make a difference in nurses and nursing. Despite constant challenges to match resources to worldwide needs, and intermittent crises, NCFI celebrates fifty years with joy, thanksgiving to God, and happy memories for many people, and moves on in Christian hope, faith and confidence towards one hundred years – if that is God's plan.

REFERENCES

Allan, J.G.M. (1965) 'Communications', *Highway* No. 16,
  July–September, pp2–4
————— (1967a) '… so let him give' (II Cor.9:7), *Highway*
  No. 22, January–March, pp4–5
————— (1967b) 'Looking to the future …', *Highway* No. 24,
  July–September, pp8–9
————— (1969a) *Highway: A short history of the Nurses
  Christian Fellowship* (Published by Nurses Christian Fellowship
  International)
————— (1969b) 'Montreal 1969', *Highway* No. 32,
  July–September, pp2–3
————— (1972) *Continuing the Highway* (Published by Nurses
  Christian Fellowship International)
Bollerud, B. (1976) 'Dansk Kristellg Sygeplejeforening', *Highway*
  No. 61, 4/1976, pp8–9
Chappell, A. (1978) 'Seven days in Suva: PACEA Conference
  23–31 July', *Highway* No. 69, 4/1978, pp8–9, 11
Editorial (1988) 'In perspective', *Christian Nurse International*,
  4(4), p3
Editorial (1989) 'In perspective', *Christian Nurse International*,
  5(4), p3
Eggo, C. (1970) 'I was there … at the Seventh NCFI Conference –
  St Andrew's, Scotland', *Highway* No. 37, pp6–10
Fish, S. (1976), 'Ninth International Conference, 3–16 August, 1976,
  held in the University of Ghana, Legon, Ghana',
  Highway No. 61, 1976/4, pp10–13.
Kettle, B. (1964) 'Looking back to Alpbach', *Highway* No. 12,
  July–September, pp3–6
Klemet, G and J.G.M. Allan (1972) 'The whole man in sickness and
  health', *Highway* No. 45, October–December, pp5–8
Lichtenberger, R. (1978) 'From my window', *Highway* no 68,
  3/1978, p3

Lichtenberger, R. (1998) 'Let's celebrate 40 years: NCFI's fourth decade', *Christian Nurse International*, 14(2), pp8–11

Lindsay, B. (1969) 'Changes in NCFI', *Highway* No. 32, July–September, pp8–9

Lovett, D.V. (1970) 'I was there … at the course for leaders', *Highway* No. 37, October–December, p11

Lynaugh, J.E. and B.L. Brush (1999) 'The ICN Story: 1899–1999', *International Nursing Review*, 46(1), p3

McFarlane, J.K. (1978) 'Nursing: the state of the art', *Proceedings of the Nursing Mirror International Cancer Nursing Conference*, (London, 1978)

Mercier, G. (1982) 'The First Latin American Conference', *Highway* No. 82, 1982/1, p15

'More impressions …', *Highway* No. 61, 1976/4, pp14–15

'News and Prayer Supplement', *Christian Nurse International*, No. 4, 1987, 1

Rosti, M. (1973) 'ICN Mexico', *Highway* No. 48, June–September, pp4–7

Scharfe, G. (2004) 'How Asia gave birth to Europe', *Link International NCFI*, 4(2), pp2–3

Siccardi, E. (1994) 'Latin America Regional Conference: News and Prayer Supplement', *Christian Nurse International*, 10(4), p2

Simsen, B. (1991) 'In perspective', *Christian Nurse International*, 7(4), p3

'Supplement' (1992) *Christian Nurse International* (NAPS), 8(3), p1

Wyber, M. (1971) 'Report of the First Regional NCFI Conference for East Asia and Pacific, Singapore', *Highway* No. 38, January–March, pp6–10, 16

PART II

BRIEF HISTORIES OF
NCFI MEMBER COUNTRIES,
2008

A group of nurse leaders in Latin America – Margaret Corin and Eunice Siccardi (centre back), who were NCFI staff, and Grace Morillo (far right), whose bicultural (USA/Colombian) and bilingual abilities have been a great gift

PACEA Leadership Conference, 1982 – Naty Lopez (back row, far left), later Regional Co-ordinator; Beverley and Alison Chappell (Front row, at either end), Margaret Hutchison (front row, second left) and Chan Kum Sum (front row, third left)

PACEA Region Leaders Group 1999 with Mary Thompson (President) and
Harry Louden (General Director), front row, centre, with some
International Board members at each side

First European Region Committee 1982: (L–R) Grace Stokes (England),
Karen Gaarn-Larssen (Denmark), Nanette Neil (Scotland), Grete Scharfe (Denmark),
Evangeline Creighton (Scotland), Helga Seeman (Germany),
Bjorg Finnbakk (Norway)

European Region Committee at conference, 1994: (L–R) Hanna-Leena Nuutinen, Catherine Robertson, Tove Giske, Uta Bornschein, Ingrid Lang Pedersen

Ezekiel Bagu, first African Regional Co-ordinator

Micah Tswabki, his successor, on NCFI staff until 2005

Nigerian leaders at Jos Conference with NCFI President Kamalini Kumar and David Parfitt, NCFI Administrator – who helps NCFI work flow well

Barkat Dass (Pakistan) with a Bible study group in India

It was often difficult for countries in CAME to function as a Region, but Dora Abraham (right) and Jessie Allen invited them to the Indian conferences, and some did attend

An international group of invited nurse leaders who met for two days at the Christian Perspectives Consultative Summit before the 1988 NCFI Conference in USA

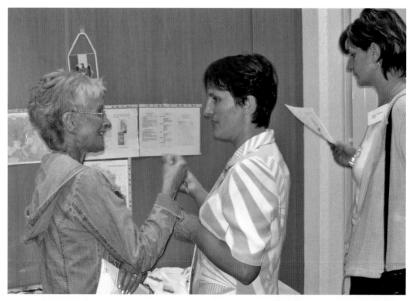

Fellowships and individuals share resources – for example Grete Scharfe (Denmark) at the Moldovan information table 2006 telling Ana Suvac about hospice care, a recently known concept in Moldova

Grete Scharfe teaching hospice care to nurses and doctors in Moldova, during a visit as a volunteer

Kamalini Kumar (retiring President) and Barbara White (incoming President)
cutting the cake with a Nigerian colleague at the 2008 NCFI
50th Anniversary Conference in Jos, Nigeria

Many nurses and student nurses go on learning, praying and worshipping …

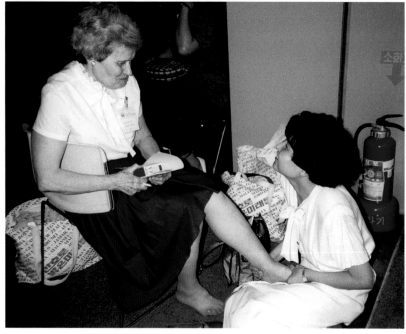

... serving patients, families and others – including colleagues
– around the world ...

... Strengthened to Serve wherever God places them, with NCFI helping to equip,
encourage and unite them in integrating faith and professional practice

NCFI MEMBER COUNTRIES, 2008

INTRODUCTION

Some of the following histories were sent in (on request) by the countries concerned, and in some cases edited or supplemented to become the length required. Some of these countries have much more extensive recorded histories available from the relevant national NCF, possibly on their website. For those countries which did not supply a history, sources used to compile one included country reports from conferences, articles or news items from NCFI publications and committee papers, staff reports and letters.

These brief histories cover only the period 1958–2008 and only those countries which were currently members in 2008. For more current information please use the contact details for individual countries which can be found on page 212 of this book; or find it through the NCFI website.

ARGENTINA

The first continuous Christian work amongst nurses began with a missionary nurse, Lois Cumming, who had worked in the country for many years. She wanted nurses to enjoy the kind of blessings she had experienced through Nurses Christian Fellowship in England, and found some Argentinians were interested. In 1970 she was seconded by her mission to NCFI, to work amongst nurses, and in 1976 was followed by Fiona Ross, another English missionary nurse. Both travelled to various cities and made contact with nurses, pastors and churches. Seminars relating Christian faith to various aspects of nursing, such as caring for dying and/or suffering people, and ethics in nursing, were well received by nurses, who expressed a need for this kind of work. Bible studies with small groups helped some to grow.

The vision was always to have Argentinian nurses leading the work, and by 1979 this became reality. Eunice Siccardi, a Christian, able and experienced nurse, was valued as a colleague and friend by both Lois and Fiona. After Fiona's sudden death following a road accident in 1978, Eunice met with others to consider the future, then heard God's call to continue the work. She left her senior nursing position and moved to Buenos Aires, and in 1979 she became the first NCFI staff member without English as a first language, working as Co-ordinator for the Argentinian NCF, Union Cristiana de Enfermeros en Argentina (UCEA); and has continued to work in Argentina (and elsewhere) since that time, both before and after her 'retirement' in 2000.

In 1979 the number of groups, mainly in Buenos Aires and Córdoba, was small. UCEA's strategy included making people aware of the nursing profession as a Christian calling and of UCEA through articles in evangelical magazines, posters in churches and bookshops, talks with Christian leaders, and personal work. *Vocación*, the UCEA journal, was also a means of communication to nurses and others. Professional contacts and attending the Pan-American Federation of Nurses Congress were also important. Opportunities to teach in nursing schools were valuable, and identifying and developing potential leaders amongst Christian nurses was a priority.

In 'Minutes No.1', the first minutes record of a UCEA meeting, it is reported that on 9 July 1982, after a Bible study, a provisional Working Committee was formed – with each member having a designated area of responsibility, such as literature or professional concerns – and with Eunice remaining as Co-ordinator. In September Matilde Viveros became President, Noemi de Motta became Secretary and Norma Bouvier the Treasurer in the Provisional Committee. At that time there were six groups meeting, intermittent workshops and visits, and a number of contacts in other places. Some American Bible studies such as 'Caring in Crisis' and 'Living in Hope' were translated into Spanish.

In 1984 UCEA held its first Constitutive Assembly and formed the first National Committee of twelve nurses, from which was elected an Executive Committee with Noemi de Motta as President. In addition to the five active groups in Buenos Aires and Mar del Plata there were other developing groups, and contacts all over the country through letters and *Vocación*. The work continued with Bible Studies and activities such as workshops, leadership courses, and preparation of a first aid course for church youth and camp leaders. UCEA has remained active and growing through the years, despite many financial and other challenges in the country.

Argentina became a member country of NCFI in 1984, and from 1979 has always contributed to the work of the Latin American Region, working with member countries and reaching out to others through visits and contacts.

AUSTRALIA

In 1913, with a committee of eight people gathering at the Royal Melbourne hospital, the Nurses Christian Movement (NCM) was first established. However during the First World War, due to the Pneumonic Influenza Epidemic of 1918, the work was put on hold. The recommencement of the work was accomplished in 1919. The objects of ANCM were 'To develop Bible study by the Study Circle Method amongst hospital nurses, and to lead nurses through Bible study to become followers of Jesus Christ'. During the early days of ANCM a position of Travelling Secretary was initiated in an endeavour to establish NCMs in other Metropolitan and Country Hospitals, and to travel interstate to encourage the commencement of branches in other States.

Once ANCM had been established in each of the mainland states, there was a more formal coming together of the state branches. A Federal Constitution adopted by mutual consent in 1928 gave state branches a common aim and doctrinal basis (recently revised and titled 'NCFA Statement of Belief') but allowed for freedom in the way the aim was fulfilled.

Unfortunately several years ago – firstly in Western Australia (WA) and later in Queensland – the state branches which had been established there in the 1920s closed. However links are maintained with individuals in those states and recently there has been development of interest amongst nurses in the Northern Territory.

In 1970 the Movement changed its name to Nurses Christian

Fellowship Australia (NCFA) in order to identify with similar organisations around the world, and with NCF International, of which NCF Australia was one of the founding members, providing its second Vice-President, Blanche Lindsay, in 1967.

The work of NCFA is overseen by the Executive Committee, with its members meeting mostly by teleconference three to four times a year. They organise General Meetings every few years to bring national leaders together in person.

NCFA in South Australia (SA)

An Adelaide branch of ANCM was founded in 1916 at the Royal Adelaide Hospital. ANCM SA met regularly during the first few years, and in 1930 a Rest Room for Fellowship was opened for nurses. In August 1931 the Rest Room closed and the Movement was virtually disbanded. In February 1937 efforts were made by Sisters from the Memorial Hospital to revive the Movement, with the support of the matron. A Council was formed in December of that year. On 4 January 1938 an office was opened and the activities of the Movement were resumed. In the early 1990s God provided a new office and meeting place. Low-key ministry to students in the universities occurred from time to time.

In 2006, after much prayer and searching by the State Council, ANCM SA employed on a part-time basis a Pastoral Care Worker to continue to reach out to contemporary nurses with the life-giving and sustaining Gospel of Jesus Christ, including running a weekly Bible study and paying regular visits to individual nurses at various hospitals around Adelaide.

NNCFA in Victoria / Tasmania

This part of what later became NCFA was established in 1913. During the boom years between the 1950s and early 1980s they organised many and varied activities, such as groups meeting in the hospitals, central meetings, pre-nursing camps and retreats held at Montrose House, a property once owned by the Fellowship and set in the hills east of Melbourne.

In the late 1980s, when nursing training changed from being

hospital to university based, a number of factors contributed to a decline in enthusiasm for, and numbers of members of, NCF. It has been proposed several times, for over more than twenty years, that the work be closed, however God has been faithful in guiding the leaders in having a Godly vision for, and strategic implementing of, this vital ministry amongst nurses.

Since 1992 a significant part of the work has been university-based student ministry and in 2004 (and again in 2006) there was employment of a Student Worker under a secondment arrangement with the Australian Fellowship of Evangelical Students (AFES).

Over the past few years it has been good to see the establishment of the Southern Health Network Bible study/ Fellowship Group whose aim is to run at least one seminar/workshop from a Christian perspective. It is independent of NCF, however some of its members have joined the Fellowship.

For a number of years now NCFA in this area has held an annual prayer brunch/think tank as its first meeting for the year and on 25 February 2006, a wonderful ANCM/NCF Reunion Afternoon was held, and later, on 30 September 2007, a luncheon was organised to celebrate the ninetieth AGM!

NCFA in New South Wales (NSW)

This branch was established in 1922 and for many years now the key focus of the ministry – established under the leadership of the long standing Director of NCFA NSW – has been the Professional Education Programme. A number of seminars and workshops are presented each year giving a Christian perspective on current ethical issues, spiritual care in nursing practice, and needs of caregivers. Study and reference material are available to NCF members and nursing students.

For some time there has been no formal work on university campuses. However NCF Council members are available to provide informal spiritual and professional support to students. Other activities include NCF district meetings in some areas of Sydney, dinners and other social events, and the AGM.

BANGLADESH

Between 1976 and 1977 four groups of nurses in Bangladesh, who met monthly for a day of Bible study and prayer, were included in NCFI newsletters for prayer. From 1977 onwards, nurses from Bangladesh were invited to the ENFI (NCF India) National Conference and in 1980 one nurse, and in 1984 five nurses, from Bangladesh attended the NCFI Conference. They were probably associate members (without voting rights) of the multidisciplinary Christian Medical Association Bangladesh, which was one of the three such associations that came into existence after partition of India. For political and other reasons, developments inside the country and contact with India were for some time difficult, and in 1992, while contact remained with NCFI, there was no NCF in Bangladesh.

However in 1996, five nurses from Bangladesh attended the ENFI Conference, and Esther Sirra, an ENFI and NCFI leader, visited the country to lead group work and Bible study. A committee was soon formed, and at the 2000 NCFI Conference five nurses from Bangladesh were present when it was accepted as a member country of NCFI.

Work continues despite problems (such as those associated with floods, and the general situation in the country), and Stacy Saha, a missionary nurse working in Bangladesh, has been an active member of the NCFI International Board from 2004. Board meetings and conferences provide an opportunity to meet, pray and plan with other board members from the Region, which is otherwise often difficult.

CANADA

The origins of NCF in Canada date from long before it was officially organised. In the 1940s a Miss Howe, from England, held prayer meetings each month in Toronto, and during that time many Bible study and prayer groups began in hospitals and schools of nursing. In 1948 Laura Adeney began to encourage and organise a Christian Fellowship of nurses across Canada, despite very uncertain finances. She began in the provinces of Ontario and Quebec, and within two years there were sixty affiliated groups from Vancouver, British

Columbia to Sherbrooke, Quebec. Others followed her in national leadership until the 1960s.

In 1980 nurses from across Canada met to pray and plan for a national Nurses Christian Fellowship (NCF) Committee. In 1981 the Inter-Varsity Fellowship of Canada (IVFC) granted the NCF official recognition, and the NCF National Committee continued to hold an Annual Meeting and an Executive Meeting each year. Representatives from most of the Canadian provinces were present at the meeting in 1991, and there were two NCF staff members, Ruth Copland in Ontario and Mary Dewar in the Mid-West. By that time NCF Committees in various parts of the country planned and carried out activities such as special worship services, dinner meetings with speakers, workshops, retreats, seminars and camping weekends. Nurse teachers and local committees in many cities and towns sponsored student nurses' groups in colleges or universities, or led groups of nurses in Bible studies and prayer meetings. Both student and graduate groups varied in size and number across the country, and video and printed materials for study were used extensively. The National and Divisional NCF Committees provided communication links among Christian nurses, and the National Committee published an annual newsletter and prayer guide. There was close contact with IVFC and also some association with other ministries such as the Christian Medical and Dental Association of Canada. An NCF presence was ensured at all the biennial meetings of the Canadian Nurses Association (CNA) and national meetings of the Canadian University Nursing Students Association (CUNSA).

After much prayer and planning Anne Workman was appointed National NCF Co-ordinator from 1992, to strengthen NCF where it existed and promote development where it was limited or absent. It was a major challenge for Christian nurses to provide sufficient support for her in this position, and for her to work effectively with nurses across the country. Attendance at Christian churches in Canada had declined and many students had not previously had opportunity to hear 'the good news'. But with the vision 'To know Christ and make Him known', Canadian NCF members were determined to see their profession transformed into one strong in spirit as well as in the art and science of nursing.

NCF Canada became a member of NCFI in 1991, and Anne Hawes' (previously Workman) report as National Director at the 2004 NCFI Conference in Seoul stated NCF Canada's mission as 'Shaped by God's Word and led by His Spirit, we desire to see the transformation of nursing students and nurses into fully committed followers of Jesus'.

NCF groups were meeting in nine out of ten provinces. Priorities were

- Building witnessing communities through reading, studying, teaching, and obeying God's Word; prayer; witness; diversity; and mutual empowerment
- Developing servant leaders and stewarding the mission of NCF by equipping potential leaders with Biblical foundations; providing coaching and mentoring; using a paradigm of risk for increasing faith development; and recruiting extra staff
- To steward the mission of NCF

Five Divisional Committees worked to achieve these priorities through city-wide, workplace, and student groups. Regions hosted conferences, retreats and workshops and a National Conference was held in Newfoundland in 2003. Attendance varied from two to three in some groups, to eighty to one hundred for special regional events. There was a focus on prayer, building global partnerships (there were two staff/student visits abroad in 2004, and on collaboration with secular professional nursing organisations.

More recently NCF Canada has faced a challenging period without an active National Director, but has continued work at home, active participation in NCFI (including a Canadian member of the International Board) and visits abroad. There is much to praise God for, which forms a sound basis for the future.

CHILE

In 1981 Gaye Mercier, the General Secretary of MOCEP (NCF in Peru), made an exploratory visit to Santiago to meet a Chilean nurse, Irma Bahahone (who had heard about NCFI at a student conference and was interested), and to do a workshop with a small group. Those present requested another meeting, which was held at the College of Nursing and attended by more nurses. After a Bible study session those present expressed a desire to learn more, so it was agreed that the study guides which had been used for this session would be left with the nurse first contacted to arrange it. In this way she or someone else could lead the group as they continued their studies.

Chilean nurses maintained contact with Gaye and, in 1982, a Chilean nurse attended the NCFI Latin American Region Conference. In 1984 groups of Christian nurses, who had been meeting in Santiago, Valparaiiso, Temuco and Concepción, formed the Asociación Cristiana de Enfermeras Chilenas (ACE), in close liaison with the Grupo Bíblico Universitario (GBU) student Christian movement. Gaye visited for three months to help to establish and extend the work by teaching and visiting. However when she arrived at the end of 1986 to help full-time as an NCFI staff worker, the work had not developed and many of the original people were no longer involved. A meeting was held to consider the needs of nurses in the country and how best to help to meet them. In addition to Bible Studies, monthly seminars were started and, while not successful in Santiago, they were popular during visits to Concepción. By 1988 a group was meeting regularly there, and another in Temuco.

These groups continued, though from 1990 there was no full-time staff worker, and in November 1991 a meeting was held to celebrate the official beginning of NCF in Chile (Asociación Cristiana de Enfermeras/Matronas Chilenas), with newly written statutes signed and the headquarters in Concepción. At that time there were fifteen active members, and eighteen to twenty affiliated, and active groups in Concepción and Temuco. By 1994 three national retreats had been held, and there were contacts in five other cities.

Chile joined NCFI in 1992, and the nine Chileans who attended the 1992 NCFI Conference in Fiji found it a wonderful experience. By 1996 there was sustained growth, including development of leadership courses. The Chilean Fellowship has continued to contribute to work in the Latin American Region, including hosting the conference in 1998.

The work has continued to develop, and at the Regional Conference in 2000 Chilean nurses presented a session on Spiritual Care and their experience as chaplains in government hospitals. (By law this service must be offered, and the nurses had put in a project to the authorities which was accepted with full support.)

DENMARK

The Beginning

The work started in 1958 with the name 'Christian Circle of Danish Hospitals' (DHK). The association was founded as a result of meetings held by Francis Grim, a South African, who was the unpaid Travelling Secretary and a co-founder of the recently formed Nurses Christian Fellowship International. After a number of discussions concerning the extension of the association, the majority of those within it agreed to it being open to all hospital staff.

The following year fifteen groups were established all over the country, and after two years, 664 copies of the association's magazine were distributed at home and abroad.

Dissolution

The committee of DHK was dissolved in 1961, due to disagreement concerning the Doctrinal Basis, shortly before they were to host the NCFI Conference at Hotel Nyborg Strand. NCFI took over the arrangements together with the few Danes remaining involved.

A New Start

Alma Hvalso Petersen, who took over as Secretary and Interim Chairperson of DHK, continued the work. In 1964 she received help from Bodhild Bollerud, a Norwegian nurse who quickly became the Chairperson and Editor for the association while working as a nurse. When disagreement at international level resulted in formation in 1967 of Hospital Christian Fellowship International (HCFI) as a separate organisation from NCFI and led by Francis Grim, the Danish association aimed at membership of NCFI.

In 1969 summer schools for young people interested in becoming nurses were established, following the model established by NCF England. Forty summer schools have been held since then, with 760 teenage girls introduced to nursing.

The work had now developed to become more relevant to nursing, rather than all hospital, staff and, in 1975, the association adopted its present name, Danish NCF (DKS), and was admitted to membership of NCFI in 1976.

The Work Grows

In 1973 Grete Scharfe was engaged first as Travelling Secretary and later as Nursing Consultant, and the DKS work was growing. Around the country groups were established and teaching was being provided in nursing schools, branches of the Danish Nurses' Organisation and in many other places. A central theme was spiritual care, which was a great interest of Grete Scharfe's. A desire to equip others to teach spiritual care resulted in development of a three-month course, with three modules focused on personal, clinical and educational aspects respectively. Each module consisted of a weekend course, self-study and practical exercises, including patient interviews. DKS played a central role in stimulating discussion on spiritual care by various means, including articles in the Danish Nurses' Organisation magazine and by co-operation to have spiritual care included as part of the curriculum in various kinds of nursing education.

Different groups have been established at times within DKS according to current needs; for example, the KNAS (Contrast to New Age in Nursing) group in 1990–93; Public Relations Committees; literature committee. A DKS file was also developed for use by local groups. The number of members was increasing, and a magazine published four times a year addressed relevant nursing themes in relation to the profession and faith. In 1980 at least forty voluntary co-workers were involved when the NCFI Conference was held in Kolding, with two hundred and fifty nurses present from thirty-two different countries.

New Seasons

After a number of years of progress with much activity and growing numbers, DKS too was affected by a change in attitude towards associations. This led to a decrease in the number of members, and more difficulty in involving members and other personnel in activities. In 1998 Birthe Kamp Nielsen replaced Grete Scharfe as staff worker, and around that time there was an effort to find possible reasons for the decline in membership, and ways in which DKS could meet the needs of nurses and other healthcare personnel – possibly in new ways. From 2001 Annette Langdahl became the staff worker.

In recent years DKS has had a fairly stable membership of about two hundred and eighty members, and has continued to meet members' needs as best it can. Some initiatives have been: co-operation with Deacon High School on a theme day for health personnel with about two hundred participants; a pilgrimage for health personnel; and dialogue and co-operation with other organisations concerning profession and faith.

In September 2008 DKS celebrated the fiftieth anniversary of the beginning of the work. There have been many discussions about the visibility of the Fellowship, and it is a recurring problem that many nurses do not know of the existence of DKS. This had led to the magazine, *Forum*, being a high priority, since it has been and remains a way of making the Fellowship visible externally, and of addressing current themes. There was also an ongoing effort to establish a web forum about Spiritual Care. Members of DKS and the staff worker have taken the initiative, are co-ordinators, and form the project group for this.

Visions in 2008

DKS wants:

- to suggest how, on a Christian basis, nurses can build nursing in a changed health system, where concepts like nearness, care and empathy have been disappearing in favour of technical and measurable nursing

- to be a vibrant, relevant and present Fellowship
- together with the members, to be in motion and contribute to development of nursing based on Christian values
- to strengthen ethical awareness
- to influence the thinking on care
- to inspire nurses to give worthy care in all the phases of life
- to inspire conscious engagement with the media
- to take part in the current debate on relevant themes
- to inspire DKS members and subscribers to engage with colleagues in dialogue and reflection

ENGLAND, WALES AND NORTHERN IRELAND

The story told is that a nurse, unable to help a dying man who asked for spiritual help, sought help from a vicar's wife, came to a personal faith in Christ, and began to meet with other interested nurses for prayer and Bible study. The news spread and groups formed in other hospitals. Certainly in 1942 the Inter-Hospital Nurses Christian Fellowship was formed, to strengthen Christian witness in nursing and bring many nurses to a knowledge of Christ. The Fellowship became active in England, Wales and Northern Ireland, and in 1967 the name was changed to Nurses Christian Fellowship (NCF), since it was not just for hospital nurses and midwives.

Over the years, activities planned by council and committees at national, regional and local level provided friendship, fellowship and support in spiritual growth for individual nurses and groups, and promoted Christian standards in professional life. Activities included conferences, seminars, lectures, and publications, which addressed ethical issues such as abortion, euthanasia and industrial action, and also 'caring for carers' at times of great change in the health service. For several years, NCF had a stand at the Royal College of Nursing Annual Conference. Some events were specifically designed for particular groups, such as nurse managers and teachers, and others were for everyone. Everyone from students to very senior nurses prayed, listened and discussed together, learning from each other and bridging hierarchical or other potential barriers. The magazine, latterly called *Pacemaker*, provided a regular means of communication. One-week residential summer school courses, to introduce teenagers to the nursing profession and Christianity, were very successful and many nurses later testified that they gained or strengthened their faith through them. Although NCF had staff workers, the summer schools were primarily led by clinical nurses and teachers during their holidays.

But over time, with many changes in nursing and society, membership and activity decreased, despite efforts to increase it. In 1995 the NCF board (which had replaced the council) decided that, in view of this and since most remaining members were retired or missionary nurses, the Fellowship should close. The final Thanksgiving Service was held in January 1996, but hope was expressed that others in the future would take up the challenge of such work and small groups of nurses continued to meet for prayer and fellowship.

In addition, with nurse education by then at university diploma level, the Universities and Colleges Christian Fellowship (UCCF) – part of the International Fellowship of Evangelical Students (IFES) movement in the UK – developed work amongst nursing students as Christian Student Nurses (CSN), supported by a full-time staff worker. Annie Leggatt, the first such worker, soon realised that, when students qualified as nurses, they still needed nursing support, fellowship and teaching on integrating Christian faith and professional life, which was not available from churches. At a UK Bible Week she began to draw together nurses from around the UK to pray. There was much interest, discussion began and, at a meeting in 1998, a new Fellowship of Christian Nurses was tentatively established. (The name NCF could not be used again for legal reasons.) The emphasis was on a national network of individual members, with local groups only as people wanted them. Newsletters were sent to three hundred and fifty contacts and to several major churches. FCN formally accepted the UCCF Statement of Faith in June 2000, aiming to become a graduate organisation affiliated with UCCF, and a constitution was written.

In March 2001, after much work and deliberation, Christian Nurses and Midwives (CNM) was launched at its first Annual General

Meeting. By November there were forty members, and by 2003 there were one hundred and twenty. But that year CNM almost died, as several founding members stepped down due to other commitments; conferences struggled or were cancelled; and finances were very low. Only Sally-Ann Foster (previously a UCCF worker with CSN) and Angela Thavaraj remained on the committee which was facing a serious situation.

Four decisions made a significant difference. First the committee asked the Council of Reference (set up in 2001) for more active support during the crisis, and two members of it joined the CNM committee (later called council). Liz Capper, a former hospital Chief Nursing Officer, became Chairman of CNM, and Steve Fouch, staff worker within Christian Medical Fellowship (CMF) for the Allied Health Professions, became Secretary/Administrator. Second the UCCF decision in 2004 to cease its specialist ministry to nursing and midwifery students led to changes in CNM's Constitution, and affected around fifty student members. Third, the CNM Council and the Christian Therapists Network (CTN) leadership, decided to hold joint annual conferences, to make best use of limited resources, and annual attendance has been between 100 and 120 since 2004. Fourth, CMF, which had worked closely with the original NCF, had supported CNM, committing resources to assist redevelopment of work amongst nurses. The CMF Executive Committee decided to sponsor three CNM members to attend the 2004 NCFI Conference in Seoul. Sally-Ann Foster (now Jenkins) had attended the 2002 European Regional Conference, which provided great encouragement for her, for the UK Christian nurses, and other European NCFs. The three CNM members attending the Seoul Conference also found great encouragement , as they recognised the wider family of Christian nurses with many common difficulties, and with much to teach and offer in support. They returned with renewed enthusiasm, ideas and vision, sharing these with the CNM Council and members, and have built contacts with nurses from Nigeria and the Philippines working in the UK.

The original NCF was a member of NCFI from 1959 to 1995. In 2005 CNM became a member, and has continued to develop, becoming a legally recognised charitable organisation in 2007. By 2008 CNM had six regional Fellowships, and links with three to four potential ones. Many more than the 180 paid–up members attend the groups and conferences, and there is now, through Facebook, an online social networking group for Christian nursing students.

The challenges remain great. But the evidence of God's faithfulness in guiding and providing through the growth of a large, active NCF, its decline and cessation after 53 years, and the birth of a new Fellowship, CNM, builds confidence, trust and hope for the future – whatever the challenges.

ESTONIA

In 1967 seven Christian nurses met in a little town called Arukula, and decided to ask God for help to form a Christian Nurses Fellowship. During those difficult years their only possible activity was prayer, due to the Communist regime. This group laid the foundation, and in 1975 they began a closer Fellowship with fifteen nurses. The aim was to unite nurses in Estonia who acknowledged Christian faith and service as a way of life.

After the political regime changed, it became more possible for Estonian nurses to go to work in Finland, and for Finnish nurses to visit Estonia. With encouragement from the President and others of the Finnish NCF, a meeting to initiate formation of the Estonian NCF was held in April 1992. Christian nurses from all over the country met for the first time, with some guests from the Finnish NCF, and made the decision that began the process of writing the constitution, statutes and goals.

A year later, at the second National Conference, the constitution was approved, a nine-member board was elected, and three members were chosen for the 'Internal Control Committee'. These people were to be responsible for the work in eight areas:

- Prayer
- Public Assistance
- Clerical Work

- Cure of Souls
- Material Care
- Information
- Training
- Culture and Music

These were to benefit NCF members, but also to extend the work to others.

The conference in 1994, celebrating the first anniversary of formation of the Fellowship, included guests from the Estonian Medical Christian Fellowship. Later in 1994 Estonia was accepted as a member country of NCFI. The NCF President, Vice-President (who was also President of the Estonian Nurses Association), and several other members attended the NCFI European Regional Conference in Finland.

The NCF work began strongly, with members distributing Bibles, organising services in hospitals, caring for old and disabled people, working with the Blue Cross to help alcoholics, and organising lectures for nurses about the Christian ways of life. However they have faced many challenges such as illness and economic emigration, and as a result, the NCF is going through a difficult time and is currently not very active.

FIJI

Nurses Christian Fellowship was introduced to Fiji by missionary nurses in 1945. By 1959 it had eight branches, and was regularly mentioned in New Zealand's items for prayer in the *NCFI Praise and Prayer* newsletters. There was prayer for nurses' needs and difficulties, and praise to God for the work of Fiji NCF's Executive Committee. In 1961 Fiji became a member country of NCFI.

The Fellowship has never had a staff worker, but has always had an active National Executive Committee, elected at the Annual National Conference. By 1992, when it hosted the NCFI Conference, there were 25 local branches of NCF Fiji, each with 10–40 members. Each local Branch Committee was elected annually to plan and co-ordinate activities and to liaise with the National Executive Committee. Activities included group Bible Studies, Leadership training courses for branch officials, Family Life seminars at local level and professional seminars at National Conferences, retreats at local and national level, and annual celebration of Nurses' Day in churches. Other activities included a quarterly newsletter, monthly prayer letters, and a monthly broadcast through the Fiji Broadcasting Commission.

By 2004 more than 36 branches were holding weekly meetings and monthly retreats, and the 3 Divisional Co-ordinators and 6 National Executive Committee members visited intermittently. In addition to activities mentioned previously, the programme in 2004 included monthly visits to the women's prison, hospital visits, the Care Ministry to residents of the Housing Assistance and Relief Trust (HART) and carol singing by candlelight. A milestone achievement of the NCF was the inclusion of Spiritual Care in the Nursing Curriculum and the Ministry of Health Corporate Plan 2003–4.

Fiji is made up of many islands and often national NCF leaders have gone to visit and encourage Christian nurses and groups on various islands, including some beyond the boundaries of the country. As New Zealand prayed for and helped Fiji in earlier years, so the Fiji NCF members have reached out to others, being involved in the PACEA Region, and sending out missionary nurses, for example two nurses who spent two years helping in Ghana. As in other countries, some senior nurses such as Lili Makutu, a past Vice-President of NCFI, have found that being involved in international professional work sometimes offers additional opportunities.

FINLAND

In the beginning four nurses prayed together

After the Second World War the Finnish nation was occupied with reconstructing the country and paying war debt, and nurses too were recovering from hard times. A group of four nurses felt spiritual thirst very strongly. They met to pray and study the Bible and began to invite other nurses to their meetings. During the summer of 1945 they organised so-called 'quiet days' for spiritual refreshment and renewal, and to provide rest from work and support friendships. There were over one hundred participants. The leader of this activity was Tyyne Luoma, who had been very involved in developing nurses' professional activities since the 1920s. She was highly appreciated for her dynamic organisation and education in public health nursing, developing home nursing and health visiting. She got in touch with Norwegian Christian nurses and from their influence SSKS, the Finnish Nurses Christian Fellowship, was founded in 1948.

Professional and spiritual communion for the good of patients

The need for God's presence in nursing was recognised, and symbolised in the logo designed for the Fellowship by Elsi Borg. The lamp of Florence Nightingale is filled with oil, the flame is formed from hands lifted in prayer, from the top rises a cross characterising God's power and the handle is formed from the Greek letters alpha and omega – Christ is the beginning and the end.

In 1949 SSKS got their first officer, a female theologian, Anja Luhtasela. She visited groups all over the country and helped to set up new ones. Monthly meetings on the thirteenth day of each month began, and there were many Bible study groups. Nurses valued co-operation with hospital chaplains and made pleas for more women theologians and more pastors to work in the hospitals. Since the 1980s there has been one part-time secretary working for SSKS. But there have been financial struggles and much of the work has been done on a voluntary basis.

Nurses aimed to spread spiritual reading material for patients by collecting money for Bibles and Christian books and newspapers, and even published a prayer calendar for daily quiet times. They organised education on spiritual matters, and also summer meetings. Staying in a natural environment and enjoying nature was to become an essential part of the annual summer meetings. Since 1970 one local group has arranged a seminar on professional and spiritual issues every autumn. ssks publishes a magazine, *VIESTI* (which means 'message') in order to keep in touch with missionary nurses also.

In 1960, after collecting for two years and taking a bank loan, ssks bought an apartment for its office. It is situated in Helsinki, the capital city, and members have taken good care of it, by many kinds of fund-raising and even bequests. The Finnish Church Council has helped ssks financially and the Finnish Education Ministry has contributed economically to *VIESTI*. ssks has joined the Church Resources Agency, which means that ssks is a part of the Evangelical-Lutheran Church of Finland, acting on an ecumenical basis.

Joining the international sisterhood and NCFI in 1987

Even in the first issue of the magazine (1948) there was material about the Lutheran Nurses Guild and Christian Nurses' Fellowship. In 1967 there was a Finnish representative at the NCFI Conference in Stavanger, Norway, and later at other such conferences.

In 1987 ssks decided to apply to become a member of NCFI, and was accepted. In 1990 there were forty nurses from Finland at the NCFI European Region Conference in Scotland! In 1994 the next NCFI European conference took place in Finland. There has been a Finnish representative on the NCFI European Committee since 1988, and Hanna-Leena Nuutinen served on the Executive Committee/ International Board from 1992–2000.

Co-operation

It is the aim of ssks to lead nurses to grow in their local parishes, so many forms of co-operation have been arranged – for example Sunday services calling especially nurses and other healthcare workers. These occasions include intercession, lectures give by hospital chaplains on counselling, and often the collections are given to ssks or to missionary work in Senegal, which has been an official partner through the Finnish Evangelical Lutheran Mission for about twenty years. Support for missionary work has been an essential, faithful and very creative part of ssks, both economically and through prayer, encouraged by news and visitors from abroad.

The Finnish Nurses' Association (FNA) invited SSKS to have a stand or arrange a musical morning prayer session during Annual Nursing Days, and in 1994 SSKS organised a one-day workshop on spiritual issues as part of these days. The FNA has supported financially those Finnish nurses who have taken part in NCFI conferences, given free advertising space in their magazine for advertising SSKS events, and local groups have co-operated, for example on events like Christmas carol singing. In addition, articles on spirituality in nursing have been published in nursing and other healthcare journals.

International Healthcare Fellowship (IHCF) representatives have visited Finland since 1953, and some seminars have been arranged with IHCF and Christian Medical Fellowship with support from a local parish.

In 2008

There were about 620 SSKS members, and 18 local groups, and in 2008 SSKS celebrated its sixtieth anniversary. There was finance for an office secretary for ten hours per week, with the board responsible for the content, editing and editorial board of the magazine on a voluntary basis. The challenges lie in calling student nurses and new members to act as salt and light in all areas of nursing. We dreamed of and prayed for a full-time nurse co-ordinator for SSKS, as well as the present office secretary. We trust, taking one step at a time, in God of whom it is written, 'Your word is a lamp to my feet and a light for my path.' (Psalms 119.105)

GHANA

The formation of Nurses Christian Fellowship Ghana (NCFG) owes much to the untiring efforts and enthusiasm of three expatriate nurse missionaries in partnership with Scripture Union, Ghana. These three, Miss Marian Aspinall from England, Miss Elizabeth Thompson from Scotland, and Miss Taylor from New Zealand, had a burning desire to start a Fellowship to fulfil the need to bring Jesus Christ into nursing in Ghana. Their untiring efforts culminated in the founding of NCFG in April 1966, at a Scripture Union 'Easter House Party' held at the Methodist Women's Training Centre in Kumasi, the second largest city in Ghana.

The National Executive Committee appointed to manage the affairs of the Fellowship included two medical doctors, Dr Felix Konotey-Ahulu and Dr Joe Riverson, who became the President and Vice-President respectively, with Miss Aspinall as Secretary. As she continued to spearhead and co-ordinate the NCF work, new ground was broken and new NCF groups started. In early 1968, Miss Johan Allan, then President of NCFI, visited and made an extensive planned tour of government and mission hospitals and NCF groups. With the national leadership she helped to draw up the first constitution for NCFG.

It was a significant event for the Fellowship when in 1968 NCFG became a member of NCFI, with NCF England pledging to partner Ghana in NCF work. In 1976 the NCFI Conference was held in Accra, Ghana and the NCFI Africa Regional Conference was also held in the country.

The appointment of a staff worker, known as a travelling secretary, to co-ordinate NCF work was useful in integrating regions and promoting regional interaction. The first travelling secretary, Miss Florence Yeboah, was an NCFG associate since she was not a nurse. She also served on the NCFI Executive Committee from 1968 until 1976, when Comfort Acheampong, a Ghanaian nurse, was elected. She was later succeeded by Mary Aboagye, and then Crystal Clottey. In Ghana, after the first appointment, nurses accepted the challenge to serve as travelling secretaries and one, or even two, at a time were supported by Ghana government secondment for many years.

The main purpose of NCFG has not changed since its establishment, but the aims have been modified,

- To seek to bring nurses to knowledge and acceptance of our Lord Jesus Christ
- To encourage all Christian nurses to be a Christian voice and presence in nursing
- To facilitate teaching which brings Biblical foundations to nursing education, practice, management and research

- To build up management capabilities of members for effective and efficient leadership
- To make continuing education geographically and financially accessible to nurses in order to increase knowledge and efficiency
- To play an advocacy role for both nurses and for patients under our care
- To encourage members to be involved in income-generating ventures for NCFG

To fulfil its mission over the years NCFG has worked with churches, parachurch groups, the Ghana Registered Nurses Association, and the Nurses and Midwives Council in training nurses and other paramedical personnel on both spiritual and professional issues.

There are national NCFG conferences, a National Prayer Day, programmes planned by the Regional and Local Committees, and work has also been done over a number of years in response to the prevalence of HIV/AIDS. This has included giving talks on HIV/AIDS in churches and communities, training HIV/AIDS counsellors, and visiting people living with AIDS to share the word of God and give food items. A typed sheet was originally used as a means of communication for the Fellowship, until it was replaced in 2002 by publication of *The Lamp* as a newsletter for NCFG. Health education manuals have also been published and it is hoped to have a website for NCFG soon.

The work goes on. In 2005 the building of the National Office was completed and, in recognition of the importance of leadership, a further commitment was made. In addition to the NCFI Leadership Training Manual, the National Council decided to adopt the Million Leaders Mandate programme. Eight nurses from different regions were trained and they then trained more than seventy others, in the hope that they would become leaders wherever they were, in NCF or elsewhere, and be effective in Jesus' name.

In 2006 NCFG celebrated its fortieth anniversary with praise and thanksgiving to the Lord.

HONG KONG

NCF in Hong Kong started with a small group of nurses who came together to pray and share their vision, and was established as an official organisation in 1960, led by three Executive Committee members. From 1962–4 there were several retreats each year to bring together Christian nurses from different hospitals. At around the same time the Evangelical Fellowship of Students (HKEFS) sent staff workers to help in nurturing nursing students and nurses. From 1964–7 groups formed in various hospitals, and six groups joined HKNCF, which in 1968 became a member of the HKEFS family.

In the 1970s a part-time worker, Ellie, was appointed by HKNCF to help in promoting the NCF ministry. As the work grew and more groups formed, two associate workers, Hester Chow and Betty, dedicated themselves to planning and running different programmes; and in 1983–4 Kiu Kwan became HKNCF's first full-time worker.

From 1975–7 the Executive Committee grew and by 1985, in addition to the Chairman, Vice-Chairman and Treasurer, there were members responsible for publications, Local Mission, Overseas Mission, audio-visual, and Spiritual Concerns, each planning and carrying out projects. In 1985 these projects included a two-month course on gospel work amongst patients, a missionary visit to North Thailand and preparation of a course for nurses on Spiritual Growth with thirteen sessions and experienced speakers. Many students found the course of benefit in their daily lives.

By 1992 the work was still growing, led by the Executive Committee elected at each Annual General Meeting. Hong Kong is a relatively small area, and there was a prayer meeting for all Christian nurses on the last Friday of each month, and seminars, retreat camps, growth groups and training courses according to the needs of the NCF groups. The activities of local groups included gospel meetings for patients, fellowship and leadership training.

Hong Kong has faced economic, social and political challenges since becoming a Special Administrative Region of China in 1997, and nurses have also been affected by medical and healthcare reforms. NCF ministry now has three areas:

- Student ministry in the three universities – where nursing students have a monthly Fellowship meeting and weekly cell groups
- Hospital ministry – links with 36 hospitals under the Hospital Authority and 4 private hospitals. Eleven of these have groups of NCF members and most have a monthly meeting.
- Joint ministry – co-operating with other Christian organisations related to healthcare

HKNCF joined NCFI in 1985, having earlier become involved in the PACEA Region, in which it is still active. It hosted both the 1996 global NCFI Conference and PACEA conference.

INDIA

NCF India, known as the Evangelical Nurses Fellowship of India (ENFI), was born with a firm belief that spiritual healthcare is an integral part of comprehensive nursing, as man (and woman) is essentially a biological, psychosocial and spiritual being.

In the 1950s an American missionary, Miss Becky Glanzer, started a Fellowship for nurses in Pune, Maharashtra. Around that time Lily Bonner, an Indian nurse, felt the Lord's call to serve Him full-time and joined Becky Glanzer in the nurses' Fellowship. But sadly, in the middle of their planning for the ministry in Maharashtra and the whole country, the Lord took Becky to glory in 1963.

In November 1964 several nurses from India and from overseas came together and worked in their respective localities and hospitals. They felt the need to unite their work under the banner ENFI, based on Psalm 60:4, 'But for those who fear you, you have raised a banner to be unfurled against the bow.'

Since then ENFI work has grown, reaching out to different parts of the nation. But India is a huge country with many spoken languages, and the work is stronger in some areas than others, and there is much yet to do. Many Christians have invested their lives in the Lord's work. Strategies to reach out and support nurses have included summer camps, Bible studies and prayer meetings, group activities and publications. In 1984 ENFI held its twentieth anniversary celebration and hosted the eleventh NCFI Conference. At this conference there were several papers on integrating Biblical principles with nursing practice, and this had a countrywide influence on nursing practice.

ENFI had joined NCFI in 1972 and Mrs Dora Abraham was an active NCFI Executive Committee member from 1984 to 1996. Dr Esther Sirra became an International Board member in 1996 and was succeeded by Mrs Chinnamma Mathew (2000–2008). Central Asia and Middle East (CAME) NCFI regional work was pioneered by Dora and Esther, and nurses from Bangladesh and India regularly come together at their national conferences. It has always been exciting as nurses from these two nations come together to worship the living God, sharing with each other and learning God's word together. ENFI has contacts in Pakistan, Sri Lanka, and Nepal, but the work has not been maintained in these countries. Political disturbance in this region is also a hindrance for the NCFI regional work. Christian nurses have been praying for a long time that a regional meeting should take place in the CAME region.

India has over one million people, of whom Christians are hardly 3 per cent. ENFI would value prayer for the Christian nurses of this vast nation to be a Christian voice and presence in nursing practice; and that ENFI will maintain the vision and touch the lives of nurses and patients with the Gospel.

JAPAN

Nurses Christian Fellowship was introduced in Japan by Dr Virginia Ohlson, an American nurse who was a General Headquarters Officer during the Allied Occupation in 1945–51. She invited two missionaries to conduct meetings for nurses for English language study, Bible study and fellowship. The nurses' group grew to over one hundred members in five years. However when the missionaries left after the Occupation, the group joined the Japan Christian Medical Association (JCMA) and ceased to be an autonomous nurses' group.

In 1969 the Evangelical Medical Fellowship (EMF) was founded. Miss Dorothy Beavan, an OMF missionary who was seeking to minister to nurses, was invited by EMF to work among nurses and care for them. In 1970 she was invited by Miss Blanche Lindsay, Vice-President of NCFI and Regional Co-ordinator of PACEA, to attend the first NCFI Pacific and East Asia (PACEA) Regional Conference in Singapore.

Meanwhile God was preparing a Japanese nurse to serve nurses in Japan. Chieko Fukushima had been working as a nurse and studying in the USA, but had become disillusioned with nursing. However she was introduced to NCF at the NCF Coffee House in Philadelphia and, through counsel and prayers of members, and attending a workshop on 'Spiritual Care: the Nurse's Role', she became aware of God's call to go back to Japan and share this important role for nurses, especially Christian nurses. While in the USA she returned intermittently to Japan, and in 1982 she moved back long-term – after which she still travelled elsewhere for conferences and other such purposes.

NCFI participated in the 1977 ICN Conference in Japan, and after this Barbara Simsen (NCFI staff) conducted seminars on 'Love that Heals' in ten places across Japan over a period of three months, and Chieko served as interpreter. Also at this time Barbara Dicks and Jean Webber, English OMF missionary nurses who were also involved in NCFI, had been working amongst nurses in Hokkaido, the northern island, since 1971.

From then on, involvement in NCFI grew. When returning from the USA to Japan in 1982, Chieko attended the PACEA Regional Conference in the Philippines, where there was one other Japanese nurse, and stayed for one month to observe NCF work. She then took up a nursing position in a Japanese university and started Bible studies amongst the nurses there.

In 1984, fourteen Japanese nurses attended the NCFI Conference in India. A year later they decided to meet for a reunion, which became the first Annual National Conference. A National Committee was formed during the fifth National Conference in 1989, and the goals and basic principles for NCF in Japan were discussed. Two years later the committee agreed to apply for membership of NCFI, and Japan

Nurses Christian Fellowship (JNCF) was accepted into membership at the NCFI Conference in Fiji in 1992.

In 1993 there were 70 JNCF members, in 10 nurses' groups and 2 students' groups, and Chieko was serving as a full-time NCF worker. An OMF missionary, Magda Breuninger, was also working amongst nurses as a co-ordinator in the Hokkaido area. By 1996 there were 14 branches, and at the fourteenth National Conference in 1998, 40 participants came from areas from Okinawa in the south to Asahikawa in the north.

Since 1998 JNCF had been focusing on helping young Christian nurses with a need for personal spiritual growth, through inductive Bible study in small groups, and in integration of their Christian faith and nursing through teaching on 'Spiritual Care: the Nurse's Role'. As a result Christian nurses have grown in their personal relationship with Christ and found an important role in contemporary nursing. They have also been helped to learn to take more responsibility and leadership in nursing, and also in their local churches. But this is a constant challenge, with a shortage of nurses and a heavy workload.

JNCF has continued to promote integration of faith and nursing. For example in 1993 the theme of the National Conference was 'Ethics in Nursing Practice: The Christian Nurse's Role', and a Christian nursing student and seven non-Christians studied 'A Biblical View of Man' together. JNCF members have continued to be involved with NCFI global and Regional conferences, and Chieko Fukushima, who has worked for so many years with JNCF either full-time or part-time, was a member of NCFI Executive Committee 1992–2000, and on the International Board 2000–04.

At the 2007 ICN Conference in Yokohama, JNCF and NCFI together welcomed many nurses and students from many countries, talking with them and gaining and giving information, including brochures. Two seminars on 'Servant Leadership: Significant power for Change' were led by Dr Barbara White, an NCFI Board Member. There were 45 nurses at the three-hour seminar with internationals, and 50 at a one-day seminar for JNCF members, with small group discussions on cultural differences in leadership. On the JNCF/ NCFI stand, the panel on spiritual care (which was based on a Biblical perspective) attracted much interest from students and nurses, including some who were not Christian, and three Japanese nurse educators asked JNCF to visit and hold meetings about it.

In addition to its value for NCFI through contact with nurses of so many nationalities, the involvement in the ICN Conference served both to make JNCF better known and to give JNCF members international experience and a broader vision of NCF and the importance of NCF ministry in professional nursing and nurse education.

JNCF goes forward with renewed commitment to the Lord, to trust and obey in love.

KOREA

The Korean Christian Nurses Association (KCNA) began in 1967, when thirty-four nurses gathered with concern for nurses who needed spiritual encouragement and fellowship. The purpose was to serve the Lord not only as individuals but as a group, applying Biblical principles in nursing and nurses' lives through evangelism, discipleship and mission.

For many years there has been strong and accepted Christian influence in Korean nursing, through both national and expatriate missionary nurses and nurse teachers. Korean Christian nurses, with an impact in both the national and international nursing communities, have witnessed to their faith.

The aims of KCNA, whose name changed in 1988 to Korea Nurses Christian Fellowship (KNCF), are:

- To help nurses to have a personal faith in the Lord Jesus Christ and grow in faith.
- To help nurses to apply Biblical principles in their work and studies.
- To promote nurses' participation in home and overseas missions.

Beginning and taking root, 1967–88

From 1967 KCNA established an executive structure with eight Executive Board members. By 1988 this included a President, Vice-President, Treasurer, Secretary, six board members and a staff worker, a headquarters office in Seoul, groups and individual members.

From the beginning KCNA organised Christian services at hospitals – Executive Board members promoted Christian Fellowships in hospitals and established KCNA branches. Bible study groups were formed, but some ceased, or joined with those of other hospital workers. However others maintained Christian meetings for nurses only.

In 1986 the first staff worker was appointed, with a new focus on small group Bible studies in workplaces, and expanded KCNA ministry amongst nursing students. Before 1986 KCNA's active members were mostly nursing leaders but in 1986 strategy changed towards attracting younger nurses, supporting small group leaders, and organising conferences for staff nurses and students. Carol Findlay, an American OMF missionary nurse, was seconded to work with KCNA. At the first national Christian nursing students' conference, Barbara Simsen from NCFI was a key speaker.

Other activities started around that time by KCNA (now KNCF) included:

- Ten Spiritual Care seminars were held
- Parish nursing seminars were held – several nursing colleges now include parish nursing in their curriculum
- Social outreach included a sponsored Christian medical mission, and visits to orphanages and prisons. Korean missionary nurses in Bangladesh were supported.

Second stage, 1989–2001

Activities during this time included:

- Integration of nursing and faith
- A newsletter twice a year and a book table at NCF events
- Discipleship, with monthly chapel and prayer meetings, regular leadership training

- Bible study and conferences
- An annual nurses' choir competition
- Professional seminars (approved for continuing education), on spiritual care and leadership

Mission outreach during this period included:

- mission prayer meetings for Korean nurse missionaries
- support for orphanages and unwed mothers at home
- collaboration with other mission groups including sponsoring (and on one occasion hosting) combined medical mission conventions in Korea

International relationships

KNCF joined NCFI in 1988, but Korean nurses were prayed for within NCFI much earlier. In 1971, Johan Allan (then NCFI President) wrote of meeting some of the many Korean nurses and aides then in Berlin, with two German nurses who started Bible study and fellowship for them. At least nine Koreans were at the 1972 NCFI Conference in Switzerland, and in 1981 Naty Lopez (PACEA Regional Secretary) visited Korea and met Christian nurses at IVF graduate camp following an invitation from Dr Susie Kim. Through that connection two Koreans attended the 1982 PACEA Regional Conference, sponsored by New Zealand and one Korean nurse, Young-In Kim, attended the 1984 NCFI Conference in India, and later became the first KCNA/ KNCF staff worker.

Three nurses attended the 1986 PACEA Conference in Singapore, including Hye-Sook Lee (currently the longest serving General Secretary of KNCF) and interest in international fellowship between Christian nurses grew steadily. NCFI leaders such as Grace Wallace, Barbara Simsen and Judy Shelly visited, met with KNCF leaders and led seminars, which encouraged nurses to integrate work and faith, and more informal ties with Christian nurses overseas were formed. Before the ICN Conference in Korea in 1989, KNCF held prayer meetings for ICN during the previous year. They also collaborated with NCFI during the event, holding morning prayer breakfasts, working at the booth and organising a Christian service at Onnuri Church to which international nurses were invited. In 2000 twenty-two KNCF members participated in the NCFI Conference in Scotland.

Third stage, 2001–2008

There was a new focus on spirituality, spiritual recovery and Christian female leadership. KNCF began to plan and pray about building a spiritual care centre.

During this time, activities held to promote integration of nursing and faith included:

- an annual newsletter
- book tables at events
- establishment of a KNCF publishing company – *Called to Care: A Christian Worldview for Nursing* by Judy Shelly and Arlene Miller was translated and published as the first book

In addition, KNCF's discipleship activities included:

- Monthly chapel and mission prayer meetings
- Volunteer training of, and activities by, Bible study leaders and helpers with programmes
- Bible study for students, staff nurses and head nurses.
- Visitation and counselling
- Leadership training
- Bible Institute for nurses, a joint project with Yonsei University Nursing College – three hours every Friday evening for two semesters (one academic year)
- National conferences twice yearly
- Annual nurses' choir competition
- Professional seminars approved as continuing education by the Korean Nurses Association
- Hosting the sixteenth NCFI Conference in Seoul, 2004, attended by over 500 participants from 40 countries
- Considering one-to-one fellowship of nurses as part of strategy, since shift patterns make gathering together more than two nurses very difficult

MALAYSIA

More than forty years ago, groups of nurses were meeting for Bible study, prayer and fellowship. Some of those nurses, like Vivien Oh Swee Choo and Ranee Pillay have remained faithful all this time.

The first decade, 1961–70, was the period in which the foundation of the Fellowship was laid. Christian nurses throughout the country were contacted and NCF groups were established in various hospitals and schools of nursing. Malaysian Nurses Christian Fellowship (MNCF) formally began when thirty representatives met at a conference arranged in 1962, and was registered to comply with government requirements in 1965. A Central Committee met bi-monthly to plan and maintain the overall functioning of MNCF, with members drawn from different parts of West Malaysia. The MNCF emblem is a reminder of the calling of Christian nurses and their values. The outer ring has the MNCF motto 'Ye are His witnesses' – the calling is to be Christ's witnesses in nursing. An open Bible with a nurse's lamp symbolises that God's word is our guide for all nursing decisions and actions. A pair of hands, lifted up between the parts of a cross, signify service for Christ.

In the first decade there were two staff workers, Miss Stella Hooi and later Miss Margaret Wyber, for East Malaysia. They kept in touch with Christian nurses and NCF groups and helped them in their Christian walk in life. By 1969 there were five officially registered branches, of which two were in East Malaysia, and fifteen established groups, with two more starting. Among those involved in these early days were Miss Ding Ling Sing, Miss Ang Poh Gek and Miss Ranee Pillay, all still involved more than forty years later. Miss Ding, as a nurse tutor, had been influencing student nurses for Christ even before MNCF was founded. Every nurse found a welcome in her home, and she was so involved with MNCF that in 1969 her home in Ampang became the MNCF Headquarters, and has remained so for many years. Local missionaries such as Mrs Angus also played an important role in visiting nurses and supporting the NCF meetings.

In the 1970s and 1980s the Fellowship continued to grow, led by the MNCF Executive Committee, and with Miss Elizabeth Alfred, Miss Ong Sim Bee (for East Malaysia) and Miss Loh Siew Heng as staff workers.

Since its inception, the MNCF Annual Conference had been the main event of the year, with Christian nurses from different parts of the country, including Sabah and Sarawak, gathering together for fellowship, teaching and encouragement in their witness for Christ. In the 1990s smaller weekend retreats were held in several different regions instead, as many Christian nurses were busy raising young families and were involved in church activities. MNCF has maintained good co-operation with the churches. With the MNCF Annual General Meetings there have often been professional talks and high tea.

In the early 1990s very few non-Muslims were admitted to Government Schools of Nursing, but just as the opportunity for providing witness to student nurses in the government sector seemed bleak, the private hospitals set up their own schools of nursing, and student contacts became mostly from the private sector. Through activities such as the continued weekend retreats, MNCF has reached out to the next generation of Christian nurses, to nurture, mentor and guide them to be effective witnesses for Christ.

MNCF is interested not just in organising events, but in the personal, professional and spiritual life of nurses. From the early days of MNCF a quarterly newsletter and a prayer circular or card were published. Later, through its magazine *The Living Witness* and Christian books written especially for nurses (like *The Christian in Nursing*) and through group Bible study, MNCF has encouraged nurses in their walk with God, and to find meaning and purpose in being a Christian nurse. Blessed with the love of the Lord Jesus Christ, Christian nurses are capable of nursing with compassion, kindness and gentleness, and Christian caring is their unique contribution to nursing. It is only through good nursing care that they earn the respect of patients and the opportunity to share God's love with patients and colleagues wherever they work.

MNCF became a member of NCFI in 1966, and has been involved in the NCFI PACEA Region and in global conferences and work. From 1980–88 Miss Chan Kum Sum, a leader in MNCF for many years, was a member of the NCFI Executive Committee, and has continued to be involved through conferences, writing for publication and in other ways. As a nurse educator before retirement and through MNCF she, like Miss Ding, has influenced the development of many Christian nurses, being known outside as well as inside Malaysia.

MNCF has celebrated more than forty years of existence and activity, with thanksgiving to God; not least for the pioneer members, staff workers, committee members and advisors, and their love for God's work amongst nurses, their sacrifices and efforts in building up the Fellowship. The prayer is that MNCF may continue to prosper for the next forty years and beyond, so that Christ may be honoured in the lives of all Christian nurses.

NEPAL

Only a very small proportion of people in Nepal are Christian, and when Nurses Christian Fellowship was started in Kathmandu in 1987 it was very difficult for them to meet for fellowship. But with the coming of democracy to the country came more freedom to have an active fellowship amongst Christian nurses. This was a real answer to the prayers of nurses inside and outside the country. Nepal Nurses Christian Fellowship (NNCF) was established at national level at the NCF's third Annual Conference, in 1991. There were five branches, at Tansen, Pokhara, Gorkha, Okhaldhunga, and Biratnagar, with a total of around one hundred Christian nurse members working in different areas of nursing.

The objectives of NNCF included providing fellowship, encouraging nurses to share their faith with others, and maintaining communication between Christian nurses locally and nationally. They also included keeping nurses aware of national and international trends and issues in health services in relation to Christian values and standards, liaising with professional organisations in the country and maintaining links between NNCF and local churches.

Locally, groups met for Bible study, prayer and discussion – for example daily prayer at tea-time, monthly Bible class, visiting different houses for fellowship and strengthening spiritual faith among Christian nurses and witness in their workplaces. The groups also supported individuals and families in practical ways, through visiting, counselling and guidance. Nationally the Annual Conference provided opportunity for nurses from around the country to come together for NNCF business, for encouragement and spiritual growth. This opportunity for wider contact and fellowship was particularly important as in many workplaces there might be only one or two Christian nurses. The theme for the fifth Annual Conference in 1993 was 'Hope, faith, love and care'.

There was ongoing active co-operation between NNCF and Hospital (now Healthcare) Christian Fellowship, Nepal Christian Fellowship, Christian Graduate Fellowship, and local churches. There had also been contact with NCF India (ENFI) and NCFI for some time, and some nurses from Nepal had attended their conferences. In 1993 Nepal became a member country of NCFI, and at a one-day seminar in Kathmandu the speakers were Dora Abraham from India, a member of NCFI Executive Committee, and Ruth Lichtenberger, NCFI General Director. Bishnu Rai, a Nepali senior nurse and teacher, and President of NNCF, was a member of the NCFI International Board from 1996–2004.

During that time NNCF remained active, but by 2008 there was less contact with NCFI and less evident activity.

NIGERIA

Foundation

In 1957 Jonathan Amao had completed training as a nurse and finished his years of bond (a system of directed placement for work) at Vom Christian Hospital in Central Nigeria. At one house he knelt in prayer with a nursing sister and prayed that God would form a fellowship of Christian nurses. His vision was so limited that he was thinking only of nurses from his hospital but God's answer was greater.

Shortly after that John Dean, the then General Secretary of the Fellowship of Christian Students (FCS) who had been visiting schools and hospitals, felt a burden to call for a standing committee of nurses and doctors suggesting that a fellowship of Christian nurses be started.

Therefore in 1960 Dr Sam Thompson, the Medical Superintendent of Vom Christian Hospital, and some missionaries decided to form the Fellowship of Christian Nurses (FCN). The first General Secretary was Ms Marilyn Morgan, matron of Egbe Hospital of the Sudan Interior Mission (SIM). The first Annual Conference was held in Kaduna (Central Nigeria), in 1961 with twenty nurses present. This was just a small beginning.

Pioneer volunteer / staff workers

FCN initially depended on volunteer expatriate missionaries in piloting its affairs.

In 1963 Marilyn Morgan was succeeded by Kay Maxwell of the Sudan United Mission (SUM). Later Jean Calder of SUM took over the role, being the first part-time travelling Secretary. In 1971 Eleanor Hatfield became her successor, and in 1973 Grace Stokes was seconded part-time by SUM to be FCN General Secretary. Ms Stokes had been involved with FCN since its inception and has known, and been known by, many nurses and midwives. She visited 140 hospitals and 32 training schools, and the Lord gave her strength and ability to cope with the situation at that time.

The Lord provided Mr Micah Tswabki to FCN as an answer to prayer in 1976, and from that point onward FCN's affairs have been managed by Nigerian nationals.

Growth and expansion

The FCN has experienced unprecedented growth over the years, and the growth and development has been both qualitative and quantitative. There are currently over 5,000 registered members and around 3,000 non-registered members. FCN can be found in 19 zones, which cover 32 of the 36 states in Nigeria. There are 150 registered branches in hospital, clinic, training institutions etc. There are now 6 full-time staff workers, and FCN is developing a national headquarters building in Plateau State, North Central Nigeria.

FCN has five trustees, and a National Executive Council (NEC) which meets three times a year to manage the affairs of FCN. There is also a National General Council (NGC), which is the highest policy-making body, and consists of NEC members, Zonal Exco Board of Trustee members, and one representative from each functional registered unit branch. They meet once a year or as frequently as the need arises.

The aims and objectives of FCN (as stated in 2004) are:

- To deepen personal faith in the Lord Jesus Christ
- To promote the application of Christian principles in nursing
- To provide regular Christian Fellowship/professional meetings
- To encourage commitment to Christian witness and mission
- To provide efficient healthcare delivery to the public
- To collaborate with local and/or international bodies which share the vision of FCN, which is to care for the whole person (spirit, soul and body)

Some important activities in FCN are:

- Annual National Conference
- Annual Zonal Conference
- Annual Leadership Training Programme
- Nurses for Life Community Initiative (NULCI) – an HIV/AIDS programme of FCN
- Impact discipleship development programme (IDDP)
- Outreach to Cameroon – a Fellowship has started in Bamenda
- Production of literature including Bible study outlines, FCN training manuals and a brochure, and also a quarterly newsletter and quarterly prayer bulletin

FCN was accepted into membership of NCFI in July 1972 and Ezekiel Bagu, President of FCN, became a member of the NCFI Executive Committee from 1976–84. At their request, he acted as co-ordinator for the Africa Region as it formed. Micah Tswabki, after being a member of NCFI Executive Committee from 1984–92, became the first full-time Co-ordinator for the Africa Region. When the International Board replaced the Executive Committee, Eno Egbe was one of Africa Region's three members from 1996-2004, and his successor in 2004, Sam Mbok, became Vice-President. The location for NCFI's fiftieth Anniversary Conference in 2008 was Jos, in Plateau State, Nigeria.

NORWAY

Although KFSS (Christian Forum for Nurses and Nurse Students) started in 1983, the idea of establishing a group for Christian nurses was not new. In 1944 an association of Christian nurses was started. One of the initiators was Ingrid Wyller, a well-known nurse in Norway. This forum was active, arranging courses and sessions over several years, and Norway was a member country of NCFI from 1963–8. But in 1967 the issue of including other health professionals arose, and it caused division amongst those in the work. The resulting association, which still exists, was the Christian Association for Health Personnel (KFH) and many nurses became members.

Ten years later, in 1977, the Fellowship of Evangelical Students (NKSS) in Norway expanded its work to include schools for professional education, including nursing schools. Thus these became an 'operation area' for NKSS, and staff were employed, with Bjørg H. Finnbakk (a nurse) employed as secretary in one region. A committee was established to focus on nurses, and arranged programmes for weekends, seminars and study days devoted to topics related to faith and professions, including optimum integration of faith and nursing. At the turn of the year 1979/1980, the visit of Bjørg H. Finnbakk to the Fellowship of Evangelical Students in the USA resulted in contact with NCFI.

Working amongst nursing students, NKSS was soon faced with the challenge of how newly registered nurses could get continued help to be a Christian voice in their profession. Should they enter another relevant association (for example KFH) or establish a new one? Delegates from NKSS participated in the 1980 NCFI Conference in Denmark and they agreed with NCFI's goal, its organisation and function. The following autumn Bjørg H. Finnbakk was employed as a national secretary to co-ordinate work among nurse students and nurses in Norway. For months there was dialogue with KFH to determine if it was possible to continue the work started in NKSS together with KFH. But KFH wanted to work with a diversity of healthcare professionals, with the aim of evangelisation and spiritual fellowship among people working in hospitals. NKSS wanted to continue its work among nursing students, and focus on the relationship between nursing as a profession and Christian beliefs and ethics. So the two associations decided to continue to work separately.

In 1982 a committee presented a proposal for a structure for work amongst nurse students and registered nurses together in NKSS, rather than two separate ones. It seemed practically, financially and administratively expedient to continue within NKSS, whose National Board accepted the proposed bylaws, and Bjørg H. Finnbakk was assigned to that work. Two study-groups were established shortly after, and the American book *Spiritual Care: The Nurse's Role* by Judy Allen and Sharon Fish (1982, NCFI USA) was translated into Norwegian.

KFSS

In autumn 1982 an Interim Board of KFSS was established, consisting of four nurses and two nursing students. Weekends and day-seminars were arranged in Northern and Southern Norway. In June 1983 representatives from the Interim National Board in KFSS and from NKSS had a constructive meeting to discuss and clarify the objectives and determine the target group. The first National Conference and General Assembly of KFSS was held in 1983, and the succeeding ones every second year. Reidun Haugen was elected as the first chairman.

In addition to seminars or conference days associated with the General Assembly, seminars and weekends were and are arranged under the auspices of KFSS in cooperation with Christian institutions and schools. From the beginning KFSS published a small newsletter for members four times a year. After twenty years, in 2003, this was developed into a quarterly journal, with the name *Journal of Faith and Profession* indicating the focus of KFSS work. The journal is distributed to all the members and to libraries at university colleges with nurse education programmes. One representative of the Editorial Board attends the quarterly meetings of the KFSS National Board (which still comprises four nurses and two students, or occasionally fewer due to difficulties in recruiting), all the work of these Boards being voluntary.

For several years the KFSS website has been important for contact with students and young nurses, and further development is a priority. In 2000 a prayer network was established, with prayer topics circulated to members. A small prayer group meets in Bergen the first Wednesday of every month.

KFSS has always given high priority to international work and connections with overseas organisations, and re-joined NCFI in 1984. Two NCFI Regional European Conferences were arranged by KFSS in Norway – in Grimstad (1986) and in Frekhaug near Bergen (2002). KFSS delegates have been active participants and speakers at European and global NCFI Conferences. Bjørg Finnbakk, Tove Giske and Karen Hagesæter have been members of the European Regional Committee, and Bjørg Finnbakk and Tove Giske have been members of the Executive Committee/International Board of NCFI.

KFSS earmarks 10 per cent of its budget for NCFI work. KFSS also takes responsibility for praying for NCFI, and especially for Spain and Romania. Supporting students to attend the international students' conferences in the European Region has resulted in new and active co-workers in KFSS.

KFSS's purpose is to:

- Unite nursing students and nurses in the workforce to help them deliver holistic care in accordance with Christian belief and ethics
- Be a Christian voice in education, the professions and society
- Ensure and strengthen the spiritual dimension in nursing theory and in nursing practice

The plan of action for 2005–7 focused on praying, maintaining contact with members, and increasing membership (which, in May 2007, was 213, of whom 7 were students).

There is also hard work to strengthen the KFSS economy in order to be able to maintain network-building and international support. KFSS presents its work externally by its journal, the website, and by courses and conferences. In 2007 a brochure was developed to recruit members and to give information about KFSS, and there are plans for posters to be used at stands in conferences arranged by other organisations, for example The Norwegian Association of Nurses and NKSS.

PAPUA NEW GUINEA

From about 1955, expatriate nurses working in government and church health services in the country established local groups of Christian nurses and students of nursing, who met for fellowship and encouragement. Because of the diverse nature of the country and poor development of telephone and transport systems, most groups lived in isolation and were unaware of happenings in neighbouring provinces or even districts. Papua New Guinea (PNG) gained independence as a country in 1976.

Many groups continued to meet in isolation, some groups affiliating with their own churches, rather than with NCF. Some groups in government hospitals had been struggling since 1976, with fluctuation in interest and commitment, and no outside encouragement.

NCF Australia sponsored at least three Christian nurses to PACEA Conferences in 1970 and 1990 and, because attendance in 1974 was not possible, to the following Australian NCF Conference. Although none of those three people were nursing in the 1990s, they all helped in the eventual formation of a national PNG NCF.

Margaret Street, a Christian nurse from New Zealand, returned to live in PNG in 1990. Her work took her to 14 of the 19 provinces in 1991 and 1992, enabling her to find the little groups and interested nurses and encourage them. By this time communications and transport were improving and nurses became organised in a Nurses Association.

In 1992 there was growing desire to form a national Nurses Christian Fellowship (NNCF), and 21 nurses from PNG attended the NCFI Conference in Fiji. They came from 6 different provinces, covering 3 of the 4 regions of the country. This group of nurses did the initial work to form a national NCF with a constitution and national office bearers appointed, and so Nurses Christian Fellowship of Papua New Guinea was formed in 1992. They also organised the first National Conference in July 1993, attended by 104 Christian nurses, from groups in 10 provinces and representing all 4 regions. The conference ratified the constitution and office bearers, who held their first Executive Meeting in October 1993. The conference also requested formally that procedures to join NCFI should begin.

PNG NCF became a member of NCFI in 1994. At that time the national NCF had more than 287 members, with 27 groups meeting weekly, and was continuing to grow. Some groups had held a one-day seminar, others a weekend camp, and the conference-planning group for 1994 had a prayer retreat before starting work. A newsletter was sent to members every three months, and a literature committee was planned to give direction and lead that work. Margaret Street continued as a volunteer staff worker, alongside her full-time job, until she left PNG in around 1996.

By 1996 there were 567 members spread over 18 of the 20 provinces (not Central and East Sepik). About 100 were expected at the 1995 Annual Conference, but 195 nurses arrived! At the Annual General Meeting it had been decided to hold regional conferences in 1996, and a national conference in 1997 asking Kum Sum Chan – an NCF leader in Malaysia whose book, *The Christian in Nursing*, was very popular – to be the speaker. There were over 200 participants at two of the regional conferences. There had been only two small groups in the islands region; but at the conference with 53 nurses at least 12 became Christians. After the conference there were members in all five of the provinces. For all three conferences the nurses chose Christian doctors to speak around the theme 'Living Word of God', using nationally prepared guidelines and nursing-related Bible studies.

In 2000 over 200 nurses were at the Annual Conference. Local groups took responsibility for leading each day, and there was a real sense of unity and desire to learn from each other and share experiences, and to make a difference in nursing in PNG.

In 2004 the stated NCF PNG aims were:

- To encourage nurses to accept Jesus Christ the son of God as personal Saviour and Lord and live as his people
- To encourage nurses to use Bible study and prayer, to develop a Christian response to contemporary nursing issues

Activities included weekly local meetings for Bible study, prayer and support; teaching Christian perspectives on nursing issues; national and international conferences; seminars on topical issues; information for members and support for missionary nurses. National conferences are held every two years, alternating with regional conferences. There is a member of the national NCF Executive Committee in each region to assist and encourage groups to function well. There is an annual membership fee, and members are asked to make a regular donation at their meetings for the national organisation. Other health workers are welcome to participate in the activities. The vision is to reach out to neighbouring island countries of Vanuatu and the Solomon Islands.

The Fellowship is growing, and in 2004 there were nearly 1,000 members, though only about half of those were really active. There were branches in all the main government hospitals in the provinces, 19 in total, and also in the mission hospitals. There was a volunteer part-time worker, but there is a need for a full-time worker to develop new programmes, visit and encourage members. The delay in appointing one was due to financial constraints.

PNG has continued to be involved in NCFI, and at PACEA and global conferences. The solid core of members who pray for and contribute financially to it is an encouragement in the Fellowship. There is also prayer for the resources to maintain and develop the work, and take the many opportunities presented.

PERU

Movimiento Cristiano de Enfermeras Peruanas (MOCEP) was formed in 1979, with an elected committee of 6 nurses and 3 non-nurses. Gaye Mercier, an Australian missionary nurse felt called to work amongst nurses full-time in Peru, and was seconded by her mission to do so as an NCFI staff member in 1976. She had been in Peru for 8 years in a different area, and began to make contacts and hold Bible Studies with small groups, at first mainly in Lima. Contacts with churches were important, and a request for help (in translating material from/to English) by the National Nursing Federation led to opportunities to conduct workshops on topics of professional interest from a Christian perspective, and to professional recognition. With short visits, teaching opportunities in nursing schools and elsewhere, and maintaining contacts, gradually activity in other cities increased.

In 1978 the first National Conference was held. As a result of that, a committee was formed to work out the shape and structure for the national movement, which in turn led to the formation of MOCEP in 1979. The two main aims were:

- to help Peruvian nurses and students to come to a personal faith in Jesus Christ
- to help each Christian nurse to relate her Christian faith to the profession

By 1980, in addition to the group meeting in Lima, there were small groups of nurses and students meeting in Trujillo, Iquitos, Cuzco, and Huancayo, and contacts maintained with nurses in four other cities. Three Bible studies on nursing topics had been prepared in Spanish. There were regular Bible study and prayer meetings, a small, well-used library of Christian literature, a 2–3 monthly newsletter, intermittent workshops, visits to other cities, and an annual conference.

In 1982 MOCEP successfully met the challenge of hosting the first NCFI Latin American Region Conference, with 27 nurses and students from 6 Latin American countries. The work in Peru continued to develop, led by successive elected Executive Committees

In 1986 MOCEP ceased to have a full-time staff worker. From 1978 the nurses had decided to contribute, and decided that MOCEP should become financially independent by 1984, but local funds were not sufficient to support a full-time worker. However MOCEP members discovered new gifts, presented a good session at the second Latin American Regional Conference, and the work continued.

MOCEP became a member of NCFI in 1980, and continued to recognise its responsibility to reach out and help other countries in the Region. However in recent years it has gone through a difficult time with little activity, and those concerned are praying for more leaders and revival of the work.

PHILIPPINES

The Inter-Varsity Christian Fellowship recognised the need for work amongst nurses, and in 1966 appointed a nurse, Nancy Ureta, for this purpose. She was joined later that year by Rosemary Chandler (née Lumm) and the NCF was established with 30 members. After 5 years of work with students there were 15 groups (9 in Manila) each holding 2–3 meetings per week, with a total of 120 members. When possible, members from various nursing schools met once a month for fellowship and teaching, also inviting friends. NCF and IVCF considered themselves as servants of the Filipino church, helping to fulfil its mission, and helping to give students a sense of missionary and professional involvement.

By 1980 there were 20 student NCF groups (18 in Metro Manila) and a graduate group which had formed in 1973, with 3 staff workers and a task force of 4 to guide them and to pioneer.

A breakthrough in professional involvement came in 1978, through participation of Mrs Felicidad Delgado, then Dean of a College of Nursing and President of the Philippine Nurses Association (PNA) A spiritual care project was developed with workshops in various hospitals and nursing schools, and copies of a translation of *Spiritual Care: The Nurse's Role* (an American NCF book by Judy Shelly and Sharon Fish) were distributed there.

By 1987 NCF was a recognised interest group of the PNA, having been accepted into membership of the professional organisation. This meant greater involvement in decisions affecting the nursing profession in the Philippines, through committees on, for example, General Welfare, Social Force, and Continuing Education. NCF sponsored spiritual care seminars during the PNA Nurses' Week, in addition to its own Annual Conference. In Manila an NCF group formed in the Armed Forces Medical Centre.

Over the years NCF Philippines has faced challenges such as the emigration of many nurses, and problems due to the political situation or natural disasters, but the work has continued.

NCF Philippines became a member of NCFI in 1972, and was

involved in the PACEA Region as it developed. Since 2006 it has been involved, with Singapore and Japan, in a PACEA Region project to work with Christian nurses and churches in Indonesia to help them to improve their healthcare, and to support the developing NCF in Indonesia.

SCOTLAND

On the shoulders of giants

The Fellowship's exact origin is unknown, but undated papers on its history claim '... we can trace the work back to 1921 when the first known group of nurses started meeting for prayer and fellowship in a Glasgow hospital'. Reference to Bessie Fraser, Martha Laird and Jean Thomson, who shared a vision for winning nurses for Christ and spent much time in prayer, shows the latter two nurses became missionaries, but Bessie Fraser spent many years visiting, writing to and encouraging nurses, persuading matrons to allow meetings, and later acting as missionary secretary and editing the NCF magazine, alongside her work as a health visitor in Glasgow. No records mention forming a committee, but by 1934 the first formal records start with the 'Aims and Reports of the Glasgow Nurses Christian Fellowship'. The three aims were:

- To help the Christian nurse in her witness in hospital by Prayer and Bible study
- To help win other nurses to Christ
- To foster the missionary spirit among nurses

The motto which had been chosen was 'All One in Christ'.

Scanty early records show these aims reflected in the Fellowship activities, with a strong emphasis on prayer, Bible study, expectation that colleagues would be (and were) led to Christ, and mission awareness with a steady flow of members to mission fields. Annual reports included information on missionary members, and reports from the hospital branches with starting dates, the earliest being

1931. These groups usually held weekly prayer meetings. Later some hospitals had a general meeting with a speaker or Bible study, often after duty on Sundays, in addition to the weekly or daily prayer meetings. Also Central Meetings or Rallies on the evening of the first Thursday of each month and, from the late 1940s, a monthly prayer time, continued for many years. Social events included picnics, outings and an annual party.

The Fellowship title soon omitted Glasgow, and a similar pattern of central and hospital-based meetings spread to other towns in the 1950s. Branches were self-regulating and self-supporting, but a General Committee met twice a year, originally comprising a student and a qualified nurse from each branch. The office bearers appointed from the General Committee, and two to three other members of it, formed the Executive Committee. The Fellowship was loosely organised, with basic business methods; but the witness, devotion to Christ and prayer of many members (some for many years) laid the foundations of an enduring NCF.

Consolidation and expansion, 1949–61

Increasing membership and spread of contacts in Scotland led to changes in the structure and management of the organisation, and contact with similar groups in England and overseas increased. *The Outpost*, the organisation's publication, was discontinued for several months in 1949 until funds were available. Publication was resumed with a quarterly magazine, at a small charge, with the title, NCF logo and a picture on the front, and including photographs, one or two devotional articles, and news of NCF in other countries, as well as NCF information, missionary news and prayer requests, and the Overseas Directory. Christian advertisements brought a small income. In 1957 *The Outpost* was replaced by a nine-page Newsletter or Quarterly Bulletin, to reduce printing costs. However in 1949, the free sample copy sent to every hospital in Scotland stimulated widespread comment and interest in starting groups.

Groups were meeting in Aberdeen, Falkirk, Dundee, and Edinburgh, though most NCF committee members were from the Glasgow area due to travel expense and time. Few NCF members could attend central events in Glasgow, but contact was maintained through the 'News from the Branches' feature in the magazine. Groups of branches were encouraged to appoint an Area Representative, who maintained contact with the Central Committee.

The Treasurer appointed in 1949 established more formal financial record-keeping, and recommended development of a Basis of Faith. This was done in 1951, and remains unchanged. Individual membership of the Fellowship, rather than just the branch, was also agreed. During Rallies held when Francis Grim visited Scotland in 1951, Miss Cathie Thomson (then Convenor of the Scottish Committee) and her sister Agnes (a non-nurse who was known to many as 'Tim') felt called to full-time work in the Fellowship, working first locally, then in 1956 as Travelling Secretaries for over two years, and in retirement they served as Area Representatives in Perth until 1970.

During the next few years there were changes to the committee structure, NCF's Twenty-First Birthday Celebration Rally, development of a constitution, establishment of an annual house party at the Keswick Convention (a large evangelical convention in England), and NCF spread to pre-nursing colleges, as well as hospitals. As membership and branches increased, an office was established in Glasgow with a full-time secretary.

Changes and challenges 1961–87

In the early 1960s membership reached over 600 individuals and 60 or more branches. But pressure on nurses from great changes in nursing and the health service made it difficult to maintain weekly branch meetings, and emphasis shifted towards the monthly area meeting, and local study days or conferences. This made the Area Representatives' role more essential, but also more difficult. The Central Committee introduced guidelines for the work, and formal interviews when appointing these representatives, and brought them together twice a year to exchange ideas and consider strategy with the committee. Financial limitations meant that there was a Travelling Secretary only from 1970–1 and from 1982–4; no secretary in the office at times; and recurring problems with the publication.

Re-grouping and re-focusing, 1987–2007

NCF Scotland had been actively involved with NCFI since its beginning, as a Fellowship and through individual members. With improved finances and a new secretary in 1987, the committee decided to host the 1990 NCFI European Regional Conference, as a way of reaching out to nurses. This was successfully achieved, but though NCF was still considered important, most nurses remained unwilling or unable to commit to membership or responsibility – difficulties shared by other organisations – and then nursing students moved into universities.

With NCF members increasingly retired or nearly so, and few new members, the committee boldly offered to host the NCFI Conference in 2000, enlisting prayer partners for unity and relationships. Despite support for conference plans, other NCF activities and membership were declining, and in 1999 NCF was at a low ebb. The 2000 Annual NCF Conference was devoted to prayer for the NCFI Conference, and the future of NCF Scotland – whether it should close. With years of prayer and work, and God's grace, the NCFI Conference 2000 was very successfully completed, with a real sense of unity. But the Scottish Committee had learned that NCF Scotland had no publicity literature, except a very outdated leaflet; most people had never heard of NCF or thought it had disbanded; income was not meeting expenditure; and Christian nurses still felt the need for support and encouragement.

From a two-day committee retreat emerged a Vision Statement applying the original aims to the current situation, and goals and strategies for the next few years derived from it. These included better-quality publicity material, a stand at as many Christian events and exhibitions as possible, targeted prayer for Christian nurses in main cities to join or start prayer groups, and an NCF website, which was online by 2001. Some strategies have not succeeded, but the fruits of others are beginning to show in the number of new members, the formation or re-vitalisation of local groups, and work with other Christian organisations.

NCF Scotland is (with Australia) one of only two NNCFs which has been in continuous membership with NCFI since its foundation in 1958. To God be the glory.

SINGAPORE

As early as 1955 Christian nurses were meeting in Outram Road General Hospital to share fellowship, in denominational groups. They later realised that a combined witness would be more effective, with a Central Committee. In March 1959 Singapore Nurses Christian Fellowship (SNCF) came into being, with the motto 'One in Christ', and in October 1960 it became a legally constituted body.

By 1969 there was a membership of 60–70, in 6 active groups spread across Singapore. Activities included Bible study, prayer, instruction in counselling, day retreats, outings, and informal meetings each quarter in the homes of members to try to reach nurses who did not live in hostels. There were also rehearsals and engagements of the Nurses' Choir, who sang at many kinds of special services, and also in local welfare homes.

NCF members were active in their own churches, and some helped in their off duty time in Christian clinics serving underprivileged people. A magazine, *Prescription*, had developed from the quarterly duplicated newsletter, and an informative prayer letter was circulated bi-monthly to SNCF members and friends. By 1985 SNCF had an Associate staff worker, and had celebrated twenty-five years of work.

Over the years there have been 'times of strength and times of stagnation and difficulty', but the work has continued. SNCF is one of the foundation members of St Luke's Hospital for the Elderly.

Singapore was accepted as a member country of NCFI in 1963, and played an active part in the development of PACEA, the first Region of NCFI. It was the host country for the first PACEA Conference in 1970, and hosted the fifth PACEA Conference in 1986, and the ninth in 2006. It has reached out to help NCF in other countries, namely Japan and Indonesia.

In 2004 SNCF had a rented office, a Central Committee planning and overseeing the programme designed to enhance the professional and spiritual life of nurses and students, and two part-time staff workers. Joanna Teoh's ministry was among nursing students and nurses, while Kim Choo was working among foreign nursing students as the Mentor Programme Co-ordinator, networking with mentors, churches, hospitals, SNCF members and students.

Since 2006 SNCF has been very involved with NCF Philippines and Japan, in the PACEA Project working with nurses and churches in Indonesia, and in training trainers to improve healthcare for the people. This was the first Regional project to receive some funding from NCFI, after the International Board approved the proposal.

SNCF approached the celebration of fifty years of Christian Nurses Ministry in 2010, and looked forward, with expectation to God, for another leap in its history.

SPAIN

Around 1961 Dr Davido Fabra, a member of the Spanish Christian Medical Fellowship (UME), invited a number of Christian nurses to meet and consider how they could co-operate with doctors and medical students to help sick people in the Evangelical community, and help one another spiritually and scientifically. This was largely as a result of visits by Mr Grim on behalf of NCFI. At a further meeting with doctors, pastors and nurses, he suggested that a Spanish Nurses Christian Fellowship should be started. This was thought to be impracticable in Spain, but fifteen nurses became individual members of NCFI.

Soon UME formed a wider organisation comprised of four parts for different groups of healthcare workers, one being for nurses and midwives, and a constitution and Declaration of Faith were drawn up, and a Directive Committee for the nurses' section was elected, with appointed office bearers. There were monthly meetings of around twenty-two nurses in Barcelona, and another small group in Valencia. The UME with its nurses' section applied for membership of NCFI and, like similar organisations elsewhere, was accepted as an associate member in 1964. However when division occurred in 1967 and Hospital Christian Fellowship International was formed, Spain ceased to be a member country of NCFI.

In 1969 the nurses' section of UME independently applied for NCFI membership, and was accepted. But for some years Spanish nurses had little contact with NCFI, which caused concern. However, in 1977, Ruth Lichtenberger, the NCFI General Director, and an English NCFI worker returning to Argentina, visited Spain and, at the Evangelical Hospital in Barcelona, they found a matron who, while in England for professional reasons many years before, had been inspired by her NCF experience, and around twenty Christian nurses were meeting monthly. These Spanish nurses knew nothing of NCFI membership, but were keen to know more. But communication continued to be scarce, and during a further visit in 1981 Ruth Lichtenberger could contact only a few Christian nurses, though they showed great interest, and prayer and concern for Spain continued. In the mid-1980s the NCFI European Committee asked the Executive Committee to arrange for the staff worker in Argentina to visit Spain to help.

Spanish nurses had attended NCFI conferences in Philadelphia (1988), Fiji (1992) and the European Regional Conference in Pitlochry (1990). Eunice Siccardi, Argentinian staff worker for NCFI, visited several times for some months in the early 1990s, and helped the Spanish nurses in Almeria, Malaga, Granada and Madrid as they began to make contact with and support each other. In January 1993 a group of nurses already involved and interested in the work met with Eunice to seek God's will for the future, and planned for as many 'triads of prayer' as possible; a Central Library of NCFI material in Spanish and Portuguese at Betel Church, Malaga; a bulletin for Spain; and networking and extension of the work, with each city 'adopting' another city to extend the work. Responsibility for the various functions was divided between the group members, and Maria Trinidad Callejon and Maria Luisa Teruel in Almeria would continue the work of keeping files of Christian nurses in Spain and sending out bulletins, a process which they had begun years ago. They would also, respectively, do the secretarial work and be the treasurer and contact person with NCFI Headquarters. Eunice taught in several workshops during this visit, while helping to prepare for NCFI representation at the International Council of Nurses Conference in Madrid, 1993 which offered many opportunities for contact between Spanish and other nurses.

In the 1990s NCF Spain enjoyed something of a rebirth – in Madrid the NCF group began to meet in different churches or homes for fellowship and to address themes relevant to the churches, such as 'New Age and Alternative Medicine', 'The Problem of Pain', and 'Evangelism and Social Work'. This provided contact with nurses and gained recognition and acceptance in the evangelical churches. A missionary in Spain, Marion Deelen, was familiar with the value of NCF work from nursing experience elsewhere, and saw this renewal of the work as an answer to her prayers. Over the following years she has worked with Spanish nurses to support and develop it. Conferences were then moved into a hospital to increase nurses' interest, with topics such as 'Infant Psychology', 'Introduction to Bioethics' and 'Stress in Nursing' presented by doctors.

Part of the NCF vision in Spain is to be of service to people in the churches, and NCF have presented workshops on 'Basic Nursing Care', 'Spiritual Care', 'Anorexia and Bulimia', and 'Osteoporosis'. NCF has a stand at Evangelical Congresses, and was at the first Christian Resources Exhibition in 2007.

Since 1998 NCF Spain has been linked with Inter-Varsity Christian Fellowship, and in the same year started a small magazine produced three times a year, which helps to maintain contact with nurses around the country. It contains articles on professional and spiritual topics. There is now an Annual Conference in Madrid for nurses from all over Spain, and regional mini-conferences run by nurses in Valencia and Galicia. In recent years there have been about 250 nurses in contact.

Some nurses from Spain have attended global and Regional NCFI Conferences, and been blessed, using some of the material later in meetings or in their magazine. A donation from NCF Norway for the magazine and prayer support was much appreciated.

NCF gives praise to God for all He has done, and trusts in His guidance, provision and enabling for the future so that NCF in Spain will be for His glory.

TAIWAN

In 1970, at the first PACEA Regional Conference, it was reported that meetings involving Christian nurses were taking place in some mission hospitals in Taiwan. At the second PACEA Conference, in 1974, a nurse from Taiwan was present. But it was not until 1982 that Mrs Katherine Han, through her own hospital work, saw the needs of nurses and was approached to start a Nurses' Christian Fellowship in Taiwan. She was encouraged by what she saw and heard at the fourth PACEA Conference that year, and took NCF materials back to Taiwan, where she shared her God-given vision with a group of Christian nurses.

In July 1983 the Nurses Evangelical Fellowship (NEF) of Taiwan was founded, with the support of the Christian Ploughman Fellowship (CPF). The aim of NEF was to serve Christian nurses while integrating their faith and nursing profession for evangelism. But in 1984, with the withdrawal of the CPF support relationship and the departure of Katherine Han following the death of her husband, NCF almost ceased. But the members decided to maintain the work and prayed. A committee of nurses from various hospitals was organised, and with God's help the work continued.

After attending the 1986 PACEA Conference, Nancy Chen accepted God's call to be the first full-time worker in NEF Taiwan. At that time NEF began to work co-operatively with Campus Evangelical Fellowship (CEF) to reach students in nursing schools. The Executive Committee of NEF was established to plan, supervise, and raise funds for its ministries. The programme included monthly meetings, Bible study groups, nurses' retreats, and occasional lectures; and, in nursing schools, contacting Christian students to start a Fellowship and an annual Spiritual Care Camp. From 1990 NEF held an annual Fasting Prayer Meeting on National Nurses Day, highlighting issues associated with nursing. NEF literature included a monthly magazine, translated Bible studies and books, and there were also videotapes for nurses.

By 1991 there was a prayer network of over one hundred nurses, and an additional full-time worker, Violet Wang. NEF also organised a team of Christian nurse who, after three months of weekly training, held hygiene and health meetings in co-operation with churches and other Christian organisations. A Christian faculty was organised to research the spiritual needs of Chinese people and spiritual care. Since then courses have been developed to teach spiritual care, up to Masters degree level. NEF is concerned with medical missions and, for example, Nancy Chen served as a short-term missionary in Niger.

In 1994 NEF Taiwan became a full member of the NCFI family and continues as an active Fellowship.

UNITED STATES OF AMERICA (USA)

In 1935 three nurses at Children's Hospital, Chicago met repeatedly to pray, and in May 1936 Christian Nurses' Fellowship (CNF) was born. It was started by the Revd John Hermann as a division of Christian Youth League (CYL), of which he was a staff member, with its stated purposes as the fullest possible development of Christian personality and character, winning others to the Lord Jesus Christ; concrete demonstration of Christianity in every relationship; and witness. CNF had a professional focus, and in 1937 began meeting at an Illinois Nurses' Association office. The word of God, prayer, fellowship and witness were key elements of each meeting. In 1939, through CNF's booth at an American Nurses' Association Conference, they discovered a CNF group meeting in Philadelphia and maintained contact.

In 1942 CNF produced a tract, 'I am a nurse', and distributed it to schools and hospitals; two hundred nurses attended the annual banquet; and groups started in other parts of the country due to contact and inspiration. By 1944 there were eleven groups in Chicago, with representatives from each forming an Advisory Committee, and a city-wide Board of Directors formed. Fund-raising was started to support a part-time field secretary, and in 1945 CNF began to share an office with the Christian Medical Society (CMS), and charge CNF members $1 per year dues. These soon increased, but in 1947 were discontinued, and members were asked to give regular donations.

The Second World War increased nurses' mobility and spread news of CNF, and, with pressures due to post-war shortages of nurses, they certainly needed support. Most meetings were devotional, there was a strong emphasis on witness, many students received New Testaments and many nurses became Christian. New groups formed, and many CNF members went overseas as missionaries. But in 1946 it was noted that the many groups in the east of the country were 'mainly poorly organised due to lack of leadership' and there was evident need for a travelling CNF representative.

In 1943, when CNF ceased affiliation with the CYL, there was discussion of linking with the Inter-Varsity Christian Fellowship (IVCF). No decision was made, but the following year the IVCF General Secretary suggested pursuing such a link, and appointing a travelling secretary. In 1946 both CMS and CNF moved their offices to IVCF headquarters, and in January 1948 CNF (which became NCF in 1952 to make it more inclusive) became officially affiliated with IVCF. Alvera Anderson, Chairperson of CNF from 1946, became the first National Secretary, soon to be joined by Tressie Myers, who became CNF General Secretary in 1950. CNF had held its first retreat in 1946, the first CNF National Conference was at Cedar Lake in 1948, the year CNF joined in IVCF's Leadership Training at Campus in the Woods.

The *CNF Bulletin* began in 1951, and almost immediately became *The Nurses Lamp*. Bible study groups were growing, and a nurses' devotional guide by a CNF founder and a Bible study guide produced by CNF staff were published in 1958 and 1961 respectively, by Inter-Varsity Press (IVP). Annual summer camps began in 1962, with fairly basic conditions. Staff numbers grew to eight or more during the 1960s, but their life was not easy. Most covered vast areas, visiting students in several states. Early staff were not allowed to own cars, or even have a permanent home. They travelled with their Bibles, and a hat and gloves to wear when meeting deans and directors. Most carried only one change of clothing. Time with other staff was rare and precious, and there was constant need for fund-raising. But there were times of good fellowship too, and hundreds of students were deeply affected by the ministry of NCF staff.

Tressie Myers brought a strong professional, as well as Biblical and missionary, influence to NCF, and when Grace Wallace became

National Director in 1968 she took NCF to a new level of professional influence. A task force was appointed to develop Christian philosophy of nursing, and the first formal research was begun to identify spiritual needs of patients. Ruth Lichtenberger, Helen McMurtry and Mary Thompson (later National Director) were appointed Area Directors, and staff numbers continued to grow (fourteen in 1973). These included, from 1976, some with a specific brief to develop materials. In addition to conferences and camps, seminars, a discipleship programme, one-day workshops and accredited continuing education began to develop, and publications continued to multiply. *The Journal of Christian Nursing* began in 1984, edited by Romana Cass, and from 1991–2005 editorship passed to Judy Shelly, an author or contributor of many of NCF publications, some of which have been translated.

The Spiritual Care Research Institute began in 1995; in 2001 Parish Nursing courses were started; and in 2002 the Institute of Christian Nursing was formed, encompassing curriculum development, research, professional forums, conferences and web-based networks. NCF has developed increasing involvement and influence, in partnership with other major organisations, in nurse education and the advance of nursing, and its publications contribute theoretically and conceptually as well as to practice in nursing.

NCF influences nursing in other countries through missionaries and through nurses passing through the USA for education, work or just returning home. It was involved in the 1956 Keswick discussions on forming NCFI, and since joining NCFI in 1970 it has provided the first General Director, four Presidents, a number of Executive Committee/ Board members and hosted the quadrennial conference in Philadelphia in 1988.

With a new National Director (Pat Emery) from 2007, (and another, Jane Hall, after 2008) NCF USA goes forward with a re-stated purpose, as a Christian professional organisation and ministry of, and for, nurses and nursing students to, 'establish and advance in nursing, within education and practice, witnessing communities of nursing students and nurses who follow Jesus as Saviour and Lord: growing in love for God, God's Word, God's people of every ethnicity and culture and God's purposes in the world.'

Defining characteristics of NCF culture have been reviewed honestly and critical needs for the present and future identified as NCF pursues its vision to see, 'Students, faculty and nurses transformed, campuses and healthcare renewed and world changers developed.'

ZAMBIA

Nurses Christian Fellowship in Zambia officially began in 1964, but groups of nurses had been meeting for Bible studies and prayer before that time. In 1964 one local group contacted NCFI to discover whether there were other such groups in the country with whom they could link. Over the next few years communication between the existing groups was established, new groups began, and in November 1971 Zambia NCF (ZNCF) came into being. A committee was appointed with representatives from eight provinces of Zambia to draw up a constitution.

In 1972 ZNCF became a member of NCFI. Ann Harper, a British missionary nurse, was the first General Secretary. The work was carried on by members of the ZNCF Committee, travelling as they could within their provinces since they all had other jobs. In May 1973 Sue Willan, also a British nurse, became the first staff worker for ZNCF, and travelled more than 23,000 miles visiting existing NCF groups to teach, train, and encourage their leaders. She also visited hospitals where students and nurses were interested in beginning an NCF group. Often Zambian nurses travelled with her, providing an opportunity for her to train nationals in NCF staff work. In 1976 Liz Wyatt (England) joined her in staff work.

In 1984 Elizabeth Halale became the first Zambian staff worker (after serving as an intern for one year). She served for two years, and later – from 1987 until 1992 – she served again. Zabe, as she was known, focused on Training Schools to start new NCF groups. During her time ZNCF spread to the Northern and Luapula Provinces, particularly in government hospitals. Among the qualified nurses, the focus was more on starting a new group and organising leadership.

Catherine Namonje, a gifted evangelist, served on NCF staff from 1988–95. By this time many of the ZNCF Committee members were Zambian nationals. Catherine also travelled far and wide along bad roads to remote hospitals to establish and strengthen groups. Elizabeth Chirwa was the first Zambian General Secretary. During these early years NCF meetings focused on Bible studies for spiritual and professional growth in the likeness of Christ, and brought much encouragement and spiritual growth to Christian nurses. But as churches began to grow there was a shift in commitment of qualified nurse NCF members to their churches. By 1995 most active groups were in nursing schools.

In June 1995 Loice Chipere joined as staff worker, after completing a two year course in Bible School. In these difficult times ZNCF had little money. NCF was now completely in the hands of Zambian nationals and travel became almost impossible due to lack of resources. A sponsored conference in 1996 left resources which covered work for the rest of the year, enabling the first visit by Loice Chipere to the Southern Province. During those hard times many contacts were lost, but the Lord was gracious in that distribution of *Quarterly News Letter* (later developed into *Solace Magazine*) continued.

Loice remained the only staff worker for seven years, during which she was appointed General Secretary, that being considered the greater need. However she continued to do the work of a travelling staff worker, which was not easy. Striking the balance between working with student and qualified nurses was difficult, but she focused on getting members to understand the mission of ZNCF and participate in its fulfilment. That mission was, and still is, to bring Jesus Christ to nurses, promote excellence in nursing, and caring for the care-givers.

In 2003 Loice was joined by two part-time staff, Isobel Kowa working in the office and Elizabeth Mulenga working as a Nurse Chaplain. In 2004–5 ZNCF enjoyed the presence of volunteer staff in short-term service, along with the General Secretary. Loice Chipere remains General Secretary, working with Isobel Kowa. Despite many setbacks, the work continues, with efforts to reach nurses and infuse Christian values in nursing, and many opportunities.

Organisation, membership, activities and finance

The ZNCF National Committee officially consists of two members from each province that has active NCF groups. Over the years it has become difficult to find members committed to the demands of Committee membership, not least due to travel costs and mass exodus to Europe and America.

Originally many student nurses who qualified became committed NCF members. Decline in qualified nurse membership began as local churches took over the role of fostering fellowship amongst nurses, encouraging spiritual growth through Bible study and prayer meetings. Some people spread misinformation that NCF was only for student nurses, and qualified nurses should join another Fellowship, which made retention of qualified nurse members more difficult.

There have been national conferences, camps, seminars and other activities since 1973, with local support or sponsorship. Zambia hosted the NCFI Africa Regional Conference in 1974, 1982, and 1998. Travel distances, costs, and sometimes strike action have reduced conference attendance. By 1995 doors opened in hospital in-service education units to hold seminars on Christian values in nursing, and reach nurses in many major hospitals. NCF members have been involved in preaching the Gospel to nurses, and have also reached out to patients and their relatives and provided them with material support whenever possible. Through churches and organisations like Scripture Union, ZNCF has provided health education, and recently trained the first Parish Nurses in Zambia.

ZNCF has received foreign support from the beginning, particularly through early expatriate staff and leadership. Members have been encouraged to give but, for whatever reason, their giving alone has never been sufficient to finance all the work which appears to need doing. However support by Zambian nationals for the work has steadily increased.

Mission Statement

ZNCF has had to review its Mission and Goals in order to remain relevant and effective. Bible studies are now tailored to help nurses with professional challenges, with care-giving as a means of opening doors for evangelism, and providing challenges to deliver excellent care. Ministry amongst student nurses is growing.

Recently ZNCF has again begun to grow, with steadily increasing involvement of qualified nurses. NCF's future in Zambia is unknown. But we hold on to the promise of God: 'He who began a good work in you will be faithful to complete it.'

APPENDICES AND
REFERENCE MATERIAL

Appendix I

NCFI PERSONNEL AND EXECUTIVE COMMITTEE/ BOARD MEMBERS, 1958–2008

Presidents	Dates	Secretary/Treasurer	Dates
Johan Allan (Scotland)	1958–1976	Margaret Smith (Scotland)	1958–1969
Grace Wallace (USA)	1976–1980	Johan Allan (Scotland)	1969–1975
Pat Ashworth (England)	1980–1988		
Evangeline Creighton (Scotland)	1988–1992	**General Director**	**Dates**
Pat Ashworth (N. Ireland)	1992–1996	Ruth Lichtenberger (USA)	1975–1994
Mary Thompson (USA)	1996–2004	Harry Louden (Scotland)	1995–2004
Kamalini Kumar (USA and India)	2004–2008		

Vice-Presidents	Dates	Other NCFI Staff	Dates
		Lois Cumming (in Argentina)	1970–1975
Anna Svea Andersson (Sweden)	1958–1967	Fiona Ross (in Argentina)	1976–1978
Blanche Lindsay (Australia)	1967–1980	Gaye Mercier (in Peru, Chile)	1976–1990
Grace Wallace (USA)	1980–1984	Barbara Simsen (HQ / Worldwide)	1976–1989
Evangeline Creighton (Scotland)	1984–1988	Eunice Siccardi (Argentina)	1979–2000
Erna Goulding (USA)	1988–1996	Naty Lopez (in PACEA)	1981–1986
Lili Makutu (Fiji)	1996–2004	Margaret Corin (in Ecuador)	1987–1991
Sam Mbok (Nigeria)	2004–2008	Micah Tswabki (in Africa)	1993–2005

Field Organiser	Dates
Francis Grim (South Africa)	1958–1967

EXECUTIVE COMMITTEE MEMBERS

Johan Allan (Scotland)	1958–1976	Chan, Kum Sum (Malaysia)	1980–1988
Agathe Burki* (Switzerland)	1958–1975	Dimity Compston (Australia)	1980–1992
Francis Grim* (South Africa)	1958–1967	Mary Aboagye (Ghana)	1984–1996
Jocelyn Perry (New Zealand)	1958–1964	Dora Abraham (India)	1984–1996
Betty Kettle (England)	1959–1984	Bjørg Finnbakk (Norway)	1984–1992
Blanche Lindsay (Australia)	1961–1980	Erna Goulding (USA)	1984–1996
Miss C Spies (South Africa)	1961–1967	Margaret Hutchison (Australia)	1984–1996
Miss E J Wyatt (Israel)	1961–1967	Nancy Larson (USA)	1984–1988
Miss P Davies (Australia)	1964–1967	Jean McFarlane (England)	1984–1988
Una Magill (New Zealand)	1964–1967	Micah Tswabki (Nigeria)	1984–1992
Dora Mettler (Switzerland)	1967–1970	Beverley Chappell (New Zealand)	1988–1992
Florence Yeboah* (Ghana)	1968–1976	Naty Lopez (Philippines)	1988–1996
Margaret Rosti (USA)	1970–1976	Helga Seemann (Germany)	1988–1992
Grace Wallace (USA)	1970–1988	Mary Thompson (USA)	1988–1996
Evangeline Creighton (Scotland)	1975–1992	Pat Ashworth (N. Ireland)	1992–1996
Grete Scharfe (Denmark)	1975–1984	Chieko Fukushima (Japan)	1992–1996
Comfort Acheampong (Ghana)	1976–1984	Lili Makutu (Fiji)	1992–1996
Pat Ashworth (England)	1976–1988	Grace de Morillo (Colombia)	1992–1996
Ezekiel Bagu (Nigeria)	1976–1984	Hanna-Leena Nuutinen (Finland)	1992–1996
Alison Chappell (New Zealand)	1976–1984	Catherine Robertson (Scotland)	1992–1996
Naty Lopez (Philippines)	1976–1981		
Josefina Nery (USA)	1976–1984	* denotes non-nurse	

INTERNATIONAL BOARD MEMBERS, 1996–2008

1996–2000

Africa	CAME	CANA
Mary Aboagye (Ghana)	Barkat Dass (Pakistan)	Erna Goulding (USA)
Eno Egbe (Nigeria)	Bishnu Rai (Nepal)	Mary Thompson (USA)
Elizabeth Kalunga (Zambia)	Esther Sirra (India)	Ann Workman (Canada)

Europe	Latin America	PACEA
Pat Ashworth (N.Ireland)	Sita de Monti (Argentina)	Chieko Fukushima (Japan)
Hanna-Leena Nuutinen (Finland)	Grace de Morillo (Colombia)	Lili Makutu (Fiji)
Elizabeth Kalunga (Zambia)	Mabel de Rivera (El Salvador)	Margaret Street (NZ)

2000–2004

Africa	CAME	CANA
Loice Chipere (Zambia)	Chinnamma Mathew (India)	Kamalini Kumar (USA)
Crystal Clottey (Ghana)	Bishnu Rai (Nepal)	Mary Thompson (USA)
Eno Egbe (Nigeria)	Stacy Saha (Bangladesh)	Anne Workman (Canada)

Europe	Latin America	PACEA
Tove Giske (Norway)	Sita de Monti (Argentina)	Lee, Won Hee (Korea)
Barbara Parfitt (Scotland)	Grace de Morillo (Colombia)	Lili Makutu (Fiji)
Ingrid Lang Pedersen (Denmark)	Margarita Riquelme (Chile)	Margaret Street (NZ)

2004–2008

Africa	CAME	CANA
Loice Chipere (Zambia)	Chinnamma Mathew (India)	Hope Graham (Canada)
Crystal Clottey (Ghana)	Stacy Saha (Bangladesh)	Kamalini Kumar (USA)
Sam Mbok (Nigeria)	Esther Sirra (India)	Barbara White (USA)

Europe	Latin America	PACEA
Marion Deelen (Spain)	Grace de Morillo (Colombia)	Chieko Fukushima (Japan)
Barbara Parfitt (Scotland)	Margarita Riquelme (Chile)	Goh, Swee Eng (Singapore)
Ingrid Lang Pedersen (Denmark)	Eunice Siccardi (Argentina)	Lee, Won Hee (Korea)

Appendix II

NURSES CHRISTIAN FELLOWSHIP INTERNATIONAL
MEMBER COUNTRIES, 1958–2008

* denotes membership current in 2008

Country	Joined NCFI	Left / Ceased
Australia*	1958	
Iceland	1958	1961
Israel	1958	Date unconfirmed – by 1970s activities and contacts had become increasingly difficult
New Zealand	1958	c. 2003
Scotland*	1958	
South Africa	1958	1967
Sweden	1958	1967
Switzerland	1958	Date unconfirmed
England, Wales & N. Ireland*•	1959	1995 (ceased); rejoined 2006
France (full member until 1964; associate member until 1975)	1959	1975
Denmark*	1959	1961; rejoined 1976
Fiji *	1961	
Spain* (associate member)	1962	1967; rejoined 1969
Norway*	1963	1968; rejoined 1984
Singapore*	1963	
Trinidad & Tobago (full member until 1964; associate member until 1975)	1963	1975
Greece	1964	1967
Jordan (associate member)	1964	1967
Lebanon (associate member)	1964	1967
Portugal (associate member)	1964	1975
South Rhodesia (associate member)	1964	1967
Uganda (associate member)	1964	1967
Ireland (associate member)	1965	1967
Malaysia*	1966	
Pakistan	1966	1993
Swaziland (associate member)	1966	1967
Ghana*	1968	
United States of America*	1970	
Austria	1972	Inactive since late 1970s except for intermittent prayer by few

• England, Wales, Northern Ireland and Scotland are four countries in one nation – the United Kingdom (UK) – but Scotland has always had a separate NCF

Country	Joined NCFI	Left / Ceased
India*	1972	
Nigeria*	1972	
Philippines*	1972	
Zambia*	1972	
Liberia	1976	Contact and activity only intermittent since late 1980s, due to civil unrest, war or other factors
Peru*	1980	
Argentina*	1984	
Ecuador	1984	Communication decreased and by early 2000s little activity reported
Hong Kong*	1985	
Finland*	1987	
South Korea*	1988	
Canada*	1990	
Germany	1992	2000
Chile*	1992	
Japan*	1992	
Nepal*	1993	
Papua New Guinea*	1994	
Estonia*	1994	
Taiwan*	1994	
Bangladesh*	2000	

USEFUL NCFI CONTACTS

NCFI Administration
NCFI Administration
11A Kirkintilloch Road
LENZIE
Glasgow
G66 4RW
Scotland
Tel: +44 141 572 4330
ncfi-admin@ntlworld.com
www.ncfi.org

Argentina
UCEA Argentina
Pico 1861 Dpto 5
1429 Ciudad Autonoma
BUENOS AIRES
Argentina
Tel: +54 114 703 2556
argentina@cidec-al.org

Australia
NCF Australia

PO Box 1062
WILLIAMSTOWN
Vic 3016
Australia
Tel: +61 039 578 1600
enquires@ncf-australia.org

NCF New South Wales
5 Byfield Street
MACQUARIE PARK
NSW 2113
Australia
Tel: +61 029 888 5842
ncfansw@gmail.com

NCF South Australia
c/o Vivienne Kitto
PO Box 54
PLYMPTON
SA 5037
Australia
ncfasa@gmail.com

NCF Victoria & Tasmania
PO Box 1062
WILLIAMSTOWN
Vic 3016
Australia
Tel: +61 039 578 1600
ncfavic@ncf-australia.org

Bangladesh
NCF Bangladesh
c/o Stacy Saha, Lamb Project
PO Parbatipur
Dist DINAJPUR 5250
Bangladesh
Tel: +88 715 268 9162
stacys@lambproject.org

Cameroon
FCN Cameroon
PO Box 818
BAMENDA
Cameroon
Tel: +23 777 139 711
ngongemelda@yahoo.com

Canada
NCF Canada
#3538
68 Corporate Drive
TORONTO
Ontario M1H 3H3
Canada
nationalchair@ncfcanada.ca

Chile
ACEMACH Chile
Avda Galnila Misral 0850
T1 Dpto 905
TEMUCO
Chile
Tel: +56 453 215 41
chile@cidec-al.org

Colombia

CECEC Colombia
Carrera 15, Calle 1288
No. 58-04, Apto 502
BOGOTA
Colombia
Tel: +57 277 9758
colombia@cidec-al.org

Denmark

DKS Danmark
Hoptrup Hovedgade 9
6100 HADERSLEV
Denmark
Tel: +45 4044 5768
dks.forum@gmail.com

Ecuador

MEDEC Ecuador
c/o Fabiola Hidalgo
QUITO
Ecuador
ecuador@cidec-al.org

England and Wales

CNM England & Wales
c/o CMF
6 Marshalsea Road
LONDON
SE1 1HL
England
Tel: +44 794 180 0637
info@cnm.org.uk

Fiji

Fiji NCF
PO Box 8173
TOORAK
SUVA
Fiji Islands
fijincf@gmail.com

Finland

SSKS Finland
Mannerheimintie 104 B52
00250 HELSINKI
Finland
Tel: +35 845 323 9697
ssksry@gmail.com

Germany

CHIP Germany
c/o Uta Bornschein
Schurwaidstrasse 8
73760 OSTFILDERN
Germany
Tel: +49 711 412 133
utavnbg@freenet.de

Ghana

NCF Ghana
PO Box KB235
Korle-Bu, ACCRA
Ghana
Tel: +23 324 467 8591
ncfghana@yahoo.com

Hong Kong

Hong Kong NCF
2/F St Andrews Christian Centre
138 Nathan Road, KOWLOON
Hong Kong
Tel: +85 223 698 512
info@ncf.org.hk

India

ENFI India
2/19 Vardarajalu Street
Egmore
CHENNAI 600 008
India
Tel: +91 442 836 4627
evangelnurses@hotmail.com

Indonesia

Indonesian NCF
RS PGI Cikini
J L Raden Saleh 40
JAKARTA, Indonesia
Tel: +62 212 355 0181
idajuniati@yahoo.com

Japan

Japan NCF
1-12-1-102, Kotake Chi
Nerima-Ku
TOYKO 176-0004
Japan
Tel: +81 033 554 9027
cf-jncf@msd.biglobe.ne.jp

Korea
Korea NCF
405 Park View Tower, 285-5
Pilwun-dong Jongro-gu
SEOUL 110-044
South Korea
Tel: +82 27 35 6378
kncf@unitel.co.kr

Malaysia
Malaysia NCF
c/o 24 Jalan Midah 11C
Tamam Midah
56000
KUALA LUMPUR
Malaysia
Tel: +60 91 318 643
kumsumchan@yahoo.com

Nepal
NCF Nepal
c/o Rebecca Sinha
KATHMANDU
Nepal
sinharebecca@gmail.com

Nigeria
FCN Nigeria
PO Box 1903
JOS, Plateau State
Nigeria
Tel: +23 480 3589 0624
fcnnigeria@hotmail.com

Norway
KFSS Norway
c/o Marte-Bygstad-Landro
Nye Saedalsvei 110 G
5098 BERGEN
Norway
kfss@kfss.org

Pakistan
NCF Pakistan
D-5, Gulshan-e-lqbal
Block 10A
KARACHI, Pakistan
Tel: +92 213 601 8121
info@ncfpakistan.com

Papua New Guinea
NCF Papua New Guinea
PO Box 844
LAE 411
Papua New Guinea
Tel: +30 167 5472 3542
bingt@datec.net.pg

Peru
MOCEP Peru
Parque Caceres 32-C
Pueblo Libre
LIMA, Peru
peru@cidec-al.org

Philippines
NCF Philippines
Suite 1420
1415 Adriatco St
Ermita 1000
MANILA
Philippines
Tel: +63 2567 3583
phebe_pendon@yahoo.com

Scotland
NCF Scotland
11 Newton Place
GLASGOW
G3 7PR
Scotland
Tel: +44 141 333 0546
secretary@ncfscotland.org.uk

Singapore
SNCF Singapore
Toa Payoh Central
PO Box 468
913116, Singapore
Tel: +65 553 3530
sncf@ncf.org.sg

Spain
NCF Espana
Apt 70 Coslada
28820
MADRID, Spain
Tel: +34 916 730 294
ncfspain@ya.com

Taiwan
NEF Taiwan
2F, No. 6, Ln 210, Sec 3
Roosevelt Road
TAIPEI CITY 100
Taiwan (ROC)
Tel: +88 622 367 0136
nef@neftw.org

USA
NCF USA
PO Box 7895
6400 Schroeder Road
MADISON
WI 53707-7895
USA
Tel: +16 082 744 823
ncf@intervarsity.org

Zambia
Zambia NCF
PO Box 71705
3 Angola Rd
Northrise
NDOLA
Zambia
Tel: +26 0262 0763
zncf-hq@hotmail.com

Nurses Christian Fellowship International (NCFI) is a charity registered with the Charity Commission for England & Wales. Registration No: 258936

INDEX